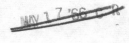

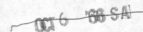

BEYOND AUTOMATION

About this book...

This volume presents a unified statement of the author's views derived from addresses before various national and international gatherings and papers prepared for legislative bodies. Some updating and adaptation have been done to reflect current conditions and to improve organization and sequence. The occasions for the speeches, which span the past seven years, are indicated at the beginning of each chapter.

BEYOND
AUTOMATION

Managerial Problems
of an Exploding Technology

JOHN DIEBOLD

President and Chairman of the Board
The Diebold Group, Inc.

McGRAW-HILL BOOK COMPANY

New York   San Francisco   Toronto   London

BEYOND AUTOMATION

*For Doris, whose patience has made possible
the addresses which form the basis
of the major part of this volume*

Automation is more than a series of new machines and more basic than any particular hardware. It is a way of thinking as much as it is a way of doing. Automation is a new *concept* —the idea of self-regulating systems—and a new set of principles. Only when our political, industrial, and labor leadership understand this shall we gain the full benefits from automation. But this kind of understanding is still so rare in policy-making levels as to be almost an isolated phenomenon.

JOHN DIEBOLD

A NOTE BY THE PUBLISHER

The name of John Diebold has become almost synonymous with automation in the past decade and a half since he first addressed himself to these problems—a startlingly brief period which, nevertheless, encompasses the whole lifespan to date of this second industrial revolution. A conspicuous pioneer in the application of electronic computers to industrial and governmental operations, he was perhaps the first to see beyond the new hardware and to recognize the full economic and social implications of automation.

The new technology is widely viewed primarily as creating employment problems. This, the author contends, is but *one* aspect of its challenge, and viewed in historical retrospect some years hence, it may appear as a comparatively minor one. He sees the new machine systems as so extending the range of human capability as to alter in a fundamental way all aspects of society. In this volume, based on his public addresses and legislative statements of the past several years, Mr. Diebold stresses the imperatives of adjusting to the new technology through imaginative innovation in private enterprise and public policy.

Certain basic facts and ideas current at the time the statements were made are so basic to the themes of these statements, as well as to the predictions they contain, that they could not be updated without interfering with the sense of this book. Nonetheless, statistical references and allusions to certain technical developments have been reviewed and updated by Mr. Diebold in the interest of current relevancy, and some adaptations and transpositions have been made to provide a smoothly consecutive treatment rather than an anthology. It is interesting to note, however, that although given in the past, the basic insights are as valid today and the suggestions are as viable as they were then.

CONTENTS

x   Contents

Part 3   THE PUBLIC PROBLEM

Part **1**

THE CHALLENGE

Chapter 1

PERCEIVING THE MAGNITUDE OF
THE PROBLEM—THREE VIEWPOINTS

The technological revolution confronting society today varies in form, and its consequences—human, business, and managerial —exceed in dimension those which are commonly perceived. The new technology is viewed as creating net changes in manpower. But this is only one aspect of the challenge, and viewed in historical retrospect some years hence, it may appear as a comparatively minor one. Machines that give the mind of man entirely new dimensions will have a far greater impact. Major social and economic innovation to adjust to fundamental technological change has become a prime responsibility of today's industrial and political leaders.

3

This chapter is based on an address given on Alumni Day at Columbia University in New York City.

4

Beyond the technological and conceptual innovations of automation lie problems and opportunities on a scale seldom encountered in human history. To meet these problems and to achieve the promise requires a perspective not often brought to bear on either public or private enterprise.

To begin with, we have yet to perceive the magnitude and the true nature of the momentous change automation is effecting in our lives, in our businesses, and in our society.

The potential and the problem of automation are far greater and quite different than yet perceived. The problem is grave and requires far more private as well as public action than has yet been proposed. Social innovation is needed to match the technological innovations.

The speed of this technological change is so great that we must today do far more than even yet proposed to ascertain:

1. The true nature of the future that is cast for us by today's innovations.

2. The magnitude and character of the problems posed for mankind by automation.

3. The alternatives open to us to cope adequately with the changes automation is making in our world.

Automation is perceived primarily as a manpower problem—involving changes in labor requirements, changes in skill as jobs change, and problems of retraining and worker mobility. Managers and workers who have experienced automation in practice know that it is more than this—that it is more often than not introduced to make possible wholly new ways of performing a task, whether that task be controlling a business, a government agency, or passenger air traffic.

Automation is all of these things. But my point is that it is much more.

Machines have always been important to us primarily in their role as *agents for social change*. We use the very term "industrial revolution" not because of the revolutionary machines of James Watt and Richard Arkwright, but because they created a whole new environment for mankind—a whole new way of life. What they gave to history was much more than the steam engine and the cotton gin, the railway and the power loom. Their machines gave society a whole new tempo, a whole new outlook.

Today's crop of machines is a far more powerful agent for social change than was that of the first industrial revolution. Today's machines result from a new found ability to build systems which process and communicate information, translate from one language to another, respond to the human voice, and devise their own route to goals that are presented to them; machine systems which improve their performance as a result of encountering the environment (machines, in other words, which learn in the normal sense in which that term is used); in short, machine systems which deal with the very core of human society—with information and its communication and use. These are developments which augur far more for mankind than net changes in manpower, more or less employment, or new ways of doing old tasks.

These are developments which mean that mankind will undertake new tasks, not merely perform old tasks in a new way. This is a technology which vastly extends the range of human capability and which will fundamentally alter human society.

The very nature of today's technology, its effect on the

building blocks of human society, will force us to reconsider our whole approach to work, to society, and to life
itself.

The technology of automation casts before it shadows of
far greater social change than were brought about by the
industrial revolution set in train by Watt and Arkwright.

Let us look, for example, at automation as perceived from
three viewpoints: that of the individual, the manager, and
public policy.

1. *The individual* perceives automation as a job threat or,
if he be a mathematician, engineer, or otherwise situated to
benefit, he perceives it as a challenge and an opportunity.

Yet automation is going to force the individual—and all
of mankind—to reconsider his very conception of himself.
As Professor Herbert A. Simon of Carnegie Institute of
Technology states: "The definition of man's uniqueness has
always formed the kernel of his cosmological and ethical
systems. With Copernicus and Galileo, he ceased to be the
species located at the center of the universe, attended by sun
and stars. With Darwin, he ceased to be the species created
and specially endowed by God with soul and reason. With
Freud, he ceased to be the species whose behavior was—
potentially—governable by rational mind. As we begin to
produce mechanisms that think and learn, he has ceased to
be the species uniquely capable of complex, intelligent
manipulation of his environment."

I am confident man will find a new way of describing his
place in the universe. Machine systems certainly show no
signs of many of the fundamental human qualities such as
imagination, volition, purposefulness, compassion, or love.
Yet my point is that man's ability to build machines which

learn, and which already possess so much of the quality we today call "intelligence," means that we have the most fundamental of changes in store for the individual and for our conception of our role as human beings.

In addition to the obvious increase in our leisure time— or, as my friend Professor Peter Drucker so aptly calls it, discretionary time—our role as individual humans is being inexorably changed by automation.

2. *The manager*, public administrator, and private businessman today perceive automation as a labor-saving device and as a means for exercising tighter control on their enterprises and making them more responsive to rapid change. The great theme in today's business literature is that automation represents an opportunity to do a better job of managing. This is all well and good as far as it goes. But in itself it tells only a small part of the story. For the significance of automation to the manager is not so much the new methods it gives him for managing—the new kit of professional tools, so to speak—but the fact that the enterprise he manages will change totally owing to the changes automation is effecting in our society.

The real potential, and the enormous problem automation poses to the manager, is that the environment in which the enterprise exists is changing, rapidly and completely. As the goals, aspirations, needs, and wants of the individual shift, and shift again and again through the human social change induced by automation, the economic realities that sustain the enterprise will change.

In other words, the great meaning of automation to the manager is to be found in the social change induced by automation. This holds a far more profound meaning to the manager and businessman than the procedural revolution taking place today in management methods. For it is in its role of serving human wants that the entrepreneurial *raison d'être* of business and government organizations lies.

Rapid and major social shifts mean an entirely new and more day-to-day role for strategic planning in guiding the enterprise. It is here that automation is making profound changes and it is here that we must look for the essence of the managerial meaning of this new industrial revolution. For here lies the heart of enterprise—ascertaining and filling human need—not the techniques of management, however important the latter may be in today's giant and changing organizations. Vitality and survival are determined by the ability of the organization, whether private or public, to perceive and fulfill these now rapidly changing human needs.

3. *Public policy* perceives automation as a problem of unemployment, retraining, and change in manpower requirements. This is altogether correct as far as it goes in dealing with the critical issue of unemployment. The additional and accurately perceived need for increased productivity occasionally produces in public policy a schizophrenic impression of calling, in effect, for "more technology—but go slowly!" But the public policy perception of automation is only too clear—if far too limited. The reality of the public policy question is that the problem is much greater than yet perceived by all but a very few.

International political as well as economic forces will require us increasingly to press for world leadership in these new technologies, which are correctly perceived by the remainder of the world as a tomorrow in which they intend to live. This necessary drive for technological leadership—on which increasingly our economically privileged position rests—will sharpen and intensify the as yet largely unperceived social problems of automation. It is significant, I think, that with increasing frequency and forcefulness statements of Soviet political and economic theory refer to automation as the means by which mankind will achieve the highest of estates. No shilly-shallying here, no confusion over whether to move forward. Rather, a firm determination to lead tomorrow where our country leads today.

Employment shifts and retraining may be easier in the U.S.S.R. but I think we would be foolish to write it off at this. Marxist-Leninist doctrine has long valued technology as a determinant of social change. It is positively *embracing* automation. Premier Khrushchev has stated, "Automation is good. It is the means we will use to lick you capitalists." But even leaving aside the Sino-Soviet bloc, the international pressure is still there to force us to pursue the technology even more aggressively than we do today. The developing nations as well as the highly developed countries of the world look to the new technology of automation as a major solution to today's problems. In addition (and this is of great significance), many of them correctly perceive automation as the key to a very different kind of tomorrow.

Pope John XXIII made a notable contribution to showing what must be done by the private sector in his encyclical *Mater et Magistra*. Governments can do much to ameliorate the human toll of transition and to help create an environment that will encourage technological leadership. But the shape of tomorrow's world is surely a problem to which we all can usefully address ourselves as individuals, working through private organizations as well as through our governments. We have hardly yet begun to face up to these aspects of the problem.

For example, the foundations, nourished in large part by increasingly automated industries, have thus far been conspicuous in their avoidance of interest in what the late President Kennedy characterized as "the major domestic challenge" of the sixties. The private foundation is an institution to which we might reasonably look for help and guidance as the private sector contemplates these critical problems.

Education is at once the core of the problem and the seed of the solution. Above all, it is the perspective of history and the insights of philosophy, religion, and the humanities that we require to perceive clearly the nature of our problem.

We have no corner on this technology even though we lead today. We can look forward only to increasing pressure from all parts of the world to move very much more rapidly in order to hold our leadership. The revolution of information technology is a revolution moved by human brains, and there is precious little built-in advantage to us other than our educational system and our major institutions of research. We will feel increasing pressure to keep ahead with both. The solution is the creation of an environment conducive to technological leadership and rapid change. The first step must be the removal of all reason for fear of individual harm resulting from technological change. But the problem cannot be solved backwards; the proper role of public policy is to create the conditions necessary to leadership in the human use of this new technology.

The electronic computer—today's crude precursor of the

machine of the future—is important not nearly so much because of the things it does today, but because it represents a new-found human ability based upon the most powerful of theoretical insights into the nature of information and its uniquely important place in our lives.

As this ability is expressed in machine systems that abstract as well as translate documents, help physicians to diagnose disease, enable lawyers to prepare briefs, and assist teachers better to develop the capabilities of their students, the world will become a far different place than it is today.

Major *social* innovation seems to me to be called for to cope with such technological innovation. It must be as rapid and as great as is the technological innovation.

During the last industrial revolution we ignored the need for social innovation. One result was Karl Marx. His ideas have had more to do with shaping the lives of all of us than we would care to believe true.

Let me revert one last time to that upheaval of two centuries ago that we now call the industrial revolution. No one in the middle of eighteenth-century England, least of all Richard Arkwright or James Watt, thought that he was changing civilization itself. Yet for us, looking back, that is precisely what was *revolutionary* about the inventions they made.

Their inventions took men off the fields and out of small shops and put them for the first time into factory life. Hence they gave us mass production, and through mass production the first civilization in history in which luxury was not confined to a few. The social change they thus set in train has altered for all time the world in which we live.

Like the pioneers of the industrial revolution of the eighteenth century, we face today a world in which only one thing is certain: change, fundamental change. But unlike those earlier pioneers, we live in an age of the greatest sense of social responsibility in all history. Our task is wisely to use our technology, our knowledge of history, and our compassion to make the age of automation a golden Periclean age in which a society based on the work of the machine—not of human chattel—rises to the full heights of which the human spirit is capable.

It is that task with which this book is concerned. In order to make a start it is first necessary to perceive the nature and magnitude of the problem and then to understand the challenge technology poses to the manager.

Chapter 2

TECHNOLOGY'S CHALLENGE TO MANAGEMENT

The accelerated pace of technological change poses a serious challenge to management. Attention is commonly focused on the problems involved in putting new innovations to work and on the imbalances created by such implementation. Perhaps even more far-reaching in its impact on today's manager is the effect technology is having on the very processes of management itself. It is becoming increasingly apparent that basic business concepts will have to be reexamined in terms of the new tools and techniques now available for running an enterprise.

This chapter is based on an address delivered before the Plenary Session of the European Community Conference of the Commission of the European Economic Community, Brussels, Belgium.

The technological changes which we have witnessed as a steady parade since the end of World War II are not a single burst originating from military work—a spurt from which we will recover. They are but the beginning of a continuum of fundamental change, a phenomenon that will continue at an increasing rate for as long ahead as we can see a future.

It is the *rate of change* itself which I believe to be the most significant phenomenon of all. The increase in the rate of change is raising problems. These problems are as yet largely unrecognized and unexplored. They are fundamentally managerial in nature.

Every factor making for change is at work to produce even more change in the future:

• *Population* increasing in what has been referred to as an "explosion"; thus the probability of innovation increases, and already we see more "simultaneous" discoveries each year that goes by.

• *Education* on a scale never before known; we are beginning to see the actuality of mass education on a high level.

• *Mobility* of a more educated population.

• *Communication* in every form, fostering an environment on the one hand receptive to change and on the other conducive to the origin of innovation.

These factors, together with increasing emphasis upon science, increasing motivation, encouraged privately and by government, are leading to a rate of change which we have difficulty comprehending.

We in the United States did not really begin to devote large scale effort to scientific research and development

17

until World War II. In 1940, a total of $280 million was
spent on research and development in the United States.
But the military stimulus of World War II increased these
expenditures to $1.8 billion in 1945 and $3.1 billion in 1949.
Most of the developments mentioned earlier are the fruits
of but the first decade of large-scale research effort. In 1961,
$16.0 billion was expended in the United States by industry,
government, and universities. Estimates for 1970 are in the
$30–50 billion range. Just think of the technology and prod-
ucts that we can begin to expect in future decades as a
result of such effort!

This increasing rate of technological change seems to me
to create some fundamental problems for management. In
part, these are problems concerning the processes by which
management puts the technology to work. And in part they
concern the way in which the technological innovations
themselves affect the very process of management.

The philosopher Alfred North Whitehead has stated in
Science and the Modern World that one of the important
facts differentiating our time is that

> . . . the rate of progress is such that an individual human being,
> of ordinary length of life, will be called upon to face novel
> situations which find no parallel in his past. The fixed person,
> for the fixed duties who, in older societies was such a godsend,
> in the future will be a public danger.

How much more accentuated is this challenge and burden
for the manager who not only must face novel situations,
but must organize his business structure so as to utilize and
incorporate constant change as a regular *modus operandi!*

The magnitude of the management problem posed by this
sudden increase in the rate of technological change has

hardly begun to be recognized as a problem at all. It is frequently viewed as a fortuitous or one-time situation, and it is attacked in a fragmentary manner in one industry after another. But it is my impression that we shall soon begin to recognize and discuss this problem as one affecting the very roots of our management philosophy.

What I should like to do is to discuss briefly four observations regarding this problem.

1. *The planning process will assume a more critical role in determining management success or failure.*

Though recently discovered by business, and still more honored in theory than practice by most managements, long-range planning is certainly nothing new to our society. The magnificent parks surrounding the chateaux of France have always seemed to me fine examples of long-range planning. In many cases the effects in composition envisioned by the original builder could not conceivably come into being until after his children had lived through the bulk of their lives. But such planning is based on complete confidence in the permanency of a way of life, or on the continuity of existing trends. What concerns me here is not necessarily long-range planning, but planning *for change* and its counterpart, planning *necessitated by change.*

The onslaught of technological change is going to focus much more attention on the planning process. It is going to place a premium upon the ability to plan effectively. A few of the reasons why this is going to happen are:

- *Product life is being shortened.* The traditional cycle of product innovation is being telescoped, not by planned obsolescence or styling changes, but by genuine technological innovation.

In many fields there is no longer time to sit back and profit by a competitor's mistakes. We may very well see a situation arise in which it is only the leader who has a chance to make a profit, not those who then copy him, for another basic change in technology will by then be taking place. As a secondary position becomes untenable, the risks of the leader increase; so must the possibility of profit or he should not enter the field.

• *The reaction time of management must shorten.* The time for leeway in adapting to new technologies has disappeared. Companies must keep track of a number of fundamental areas of scientific work and must react rapidly to apply this work when the time is right. They must consciously plan to be the ones who obsolesce not only their own products, but their very industries. A few recent and dramatic developments may be cited:

a. The laser: a new component growing out of a union of electronics and optics which makes possible an entirely new means of long distance communications through storage of electronic energy in a crystal and discharge as a high energy burst of light (visible or invisible to the human eye, as we will).

b. Cryogenics: or ultra low temperature electronics, where great increases become possible in speed of data storage and retrieval.

c. Molelectronics: an incredible phenomenon—substitution of the structure of the molecule itself as electronic circuitry in place of the subminiature component circuitry that is today considered the most advanced of methods.

• *The life of business and industrial processes, as well as products, are being both shortened and changed.*

Much of the new technology, particularly that part of it dealing with information processing, profoundly changes the manner in which business is conducted.

For example, the American Telephone and Telegraph Company expects communication between machines in different cities to exceed voice communication over telephone lines by 1970. The consequences of such a change are staggering, not only for the telephone system, but for the procedures by which the remainder of United States business is conducted. It is only through a high order of planning that such a rate of change can be made to benefit a firm rather than its competitor.

- *The increased complexity* and tightened interrelationship of functions within a single organization, together with the ever more complex relationships with other organizations, means that successful—and successful is increasingly coming to mean rapid—adjustment to change is impossible without a high order skill in planning.

For these reasons, and many more, I believe that planning as a *process* is a subject to which more attention must be given by business management.

2. *Effective management of creative and service personnel is becoming an important determinant of business success.*

While the early part of this century saw an employment shift in the United States from the farm to the factory, the 1950s brought a shift from the factory to the office. In 1959 only 30 per cent of the United States gross national product was the result of manufacturing. Over 45 per cent was value added by transport, commerce, and other *service* activities, not including government. Even with manufacturing, the factory worker is being replaced by clerical, technical, and managerial employees. Managerial, professional, and technical personnel alone increased from 7.4 per cent of manufacturing employment in 1940 to 12.7 per cent in 1959. This shift in the employment structure has occasioned an entire nexus of problems in how to manage service, technical, creative, and management personnel.

Our methods of management have not kept pace with this shift. America has entered this era with a legacy of concepts developed to meet the needs of the unskilled worker.

The results of labor-management relations to date might be summarized as the guarantee of equal treatment and the expectation of average performance. These concepts are already recognized as archaic in dealing with creative personnel. What must be encouraged is exceptional performance, and what may well be needed is individualized treatment.

The problems in this area are substantial and numerous. One is that the product, an idea, is so difficult to schedule; another is that scientists tend to direct their prime loyalty to their professions, rather than to their employers; a third is the magnitude of the task of integrating what must remain individualized effort; and a fourth, the lack of standards to measure performance.

There is also a communication impediment growing out of the diversity of background and aggravated by the growing interdependence of science and management. Studies in human relations have done much to give us insight into the human requirements of effective organization. But this falls short of what is needed.

Too often management unconsciously assumes that spending a given percentage on research, or creating fine working conditions, will produce results. The prerequisites of genius follow—not precede—the essence of genius. Too often this fact is lost sight of. The fine equipment, campus-like plants, and company-paid university courses are but empty trappings if the human quality and the proper leadership are not already present. Many managements have yet to understand the essence of the task. The rewards of those that do will be greater as change increases.

3. *Many accepted business concepts must change.*

Even as fundamental a change as the definition of a business can change through rapid shifts in technology. Peter Drucker, in his book *The Practice of Management,* states: "There is only one valid definition of business purpose: to create a customer. . . . Any business enterprise has two—and only these two—basic functions: marketing and innovation." Examples are all about us:

• *The packaging of equity investment with standard life insurance* is in recognition of growing customer need for inflation protection.

• *A company manufacturing calculating machines* had best view itself as being in the information handling business. It should remain in the forefront of what a few years ago would have seemed an unrelated technology, or it may not remain in business for long.

• *If the motion picture industry had defined its business* as the supply of entertainment rather than only film entertainment, it might now be the heart of the television industry rather than a contract supplier to it.

Among the other business concepts that must change are:

• *Return on investment must be higher in these new*

fields in order to justify the increased risk. Conversely, business must take bigger risks for sufficient return when technological change is great. A case in point is the computer business itself. The costs of entering this new industry have exceeded everyone's expectation. Those manufacturers who have planned for a low rate of return have already been forced out of the business.

• *Management may have to take a longer run view of profits.* Instead of planning for a fixed per cent return per year, it may well be necessary to reorient aims to a per cent of profit over a given business cycle. (It is also possible, of course, that as labor becomes more fixed there may be a resultant lessening of cyclical business patterns.)

• *The concepts of overhead and of labor productivity must change* as the direct laborer disappears. Allocation of overhead costs must reflect the tremendous and disproportionate increase in productivity of some sectors of a business.

• *The traditional office-plant distinction requires overhaul* as production is increasingly controlled by a business-wide information system through computer scheduling and actual factory control.

• *The role of middle management will change* as the function of allocation of resources is performed by computers. Some predict the disappearance of middle management as a line function and the growth of a new staffing function—the analysis and continuing reappraisal of the computer models and of the assumptions on which they are based in order to keep the system sensitive and itself receptive to change.

• *Management has a capacity never possible before either to centralize or decentralize its decision functions.* The advances made in communications, among machines as well as people, now allow for direct, cheap, and immediate flow and feedback of information among any geographic points. Whether or not centralization is appropriate will vary with the situation, but the decision need no longer fall automatically to decentralization.

4. *The new technology is itself changing the process of management.*

The technology of information handling, communications, control, related developments in information theory, at first applied crudely to the mechanization of work already performed manually, contains within it the basis for not only substantially changing the process of management, but for extending the range of man's capability. It is a development we are only beginning to understand.

In 1950 when computers were new, it seemed to many that they were only useful for scientific purposes. One projection estimated the need for about a dozen in the United States. That was ten years ago. Today we have over 15,000 computers at work. The projections of my own firm are that after 1965, there will be about 20,000 computers installed in the United States alone.

We are today using this technology in only the most elementary manner. New techniques utilizing computer capabilities are just beginning to appear on the business scene. Operations research (the building of mathematical models to solve business problems), simulation (using the computer to supply "what would happen if" answers to decision alternatives), and gaming theory (to plan strategically in competitive markets) are but a few.

The magnitude of change in business organization which

will be brought about by this technology is far greater than most of us today recognize. For example, today's business organization structure is a legacy of the first industrial revolution in which specialization of labor was followed by mechanization around specialties. We are now in possession of technology which allows us to build information systems which transcend the compartmentalized structure of business organization. Much of the difficulty that we have been experiencing in putting these new tools to work in recent years results from the fact that it clashes with our fundamental organization system. This is a problem that is not yet recognized by many of the organizations experiencing it. I know because my firm is regularly called upon to solve problems which are really symptoms of this more fundamental organizational conflict.

The challenge to management posed by technology is a challenge of basic theory as well as of operation. It is here that United States business is having the greatest difficulties in effectively putting the new technology to work. It is possible that our educational system, which is empirically based, needs a more theoretical orientation.

These observations may help to illustrate the type of management problem that is being raised by the pace of today's technological change.

I would like to turn briefly to another type of change— social change—which is at the same time a result of the technological change and the cause of its own set of management problems.

As important as technological change is, we must recognize that technology is merely an agent for social change. Social change will in turn result in more profound conse-

quences for business than the technological change which spawned it. I would like to make just two observations on social change.

1. *Management must look to social change as an active agent in business planning.*

Management has always known that changes in social structure change consumer demand. But as the rate of such social change increases—and it will change as fast as the technology—management must be able to anticipate such shifts and react with increasing speed. Some of these changes, as I see them, are:

• *The tremendous increase in the standard of living* (brought about by technological change) is creating whole new industries in discretionary goods—entertainment, sports, books, travel, service—and it is predicted that by 1970 over half of disposable income in the United States will be discretionary.

• *The redistribution of wealth*—with the tremendous growth of the middle class—is creating a demand for higher quality durable goods.

• *Changes in taste* will foster redesign of products; even the chrome on our cars is disappearing.

• *Shifts in population mix*, with a disproportionate increase in the old and young, will require new consumer orientation (in the next ten years we expect the group under 25 to increase 46 per cent; the group over 45 to increase 20 per cent; and the group between 35–44 to decrease 1 per cent).

• *The decline in servants* is in part responsible for the growth of the appliance industry.

• *The growth of suburbia,* made possible by the automobile, has in turn created the shopping center and brought about not the supermarket but new distribution methods to service the supermarket (and also the decline in older marketing methods, such as the mail-order catalog).

• *Increased leisure* has not only created new industries, such as do-it-yourself, but changed old ones: last year Americans purchased twice as many books as ten years ago. We now spend more on classical records than on baseball, our national sport.

2. *Key to the social burden of change is education.*

Economic growth depends on change. However, the transitional burdens of social change cannot be borne by labor or management or government alone, but only by the joint efforts of all. The main burden is education and re-education, not only of the labor force, but of management and technical personnel as well.

I am happy to say that some recent progress has been made, at least in recognition of this problem. For example:

• *The Pacific Maritime Association,* in a contract recently negotiated with the International Longshoremen's Union, agreed to contribute up to $5 million a year from savings resulting from new methods to a union operated fund with which to offset hardships resulting from technological unemployment.

• *A local of the International Brotherhood of Electrical Workers,* in cooperation with the Federal Office of Apprentice Training and a local vocational school, has set up what it calls a "post-graduate school" for training in new electrical techniques because they are convinced that jobs will be created by the introduction of automation.

• *The Manpower Development and Training Act* became

operative in its early stages in July, 1962. It represents a $435 million program to train, retrain, and upgrade the skills of workers who are subject to unemployment or underemployment. This legislation represents a far-reaching experiment in an area in which the United States has lagged far behind the Western European and Scandinavian countries. It represents a tangible recognition that the Federal government must assume responsibility for easing the burden that automation and other technological advances bring to individual workers and, in some cases, to whole communities. Business managements have a tremendous stake in becoming familiar with this program and availing themselves of the opportunities it presents.

If we consider what management *has* accomplished, that management can rise to the challenge of social change is hardly in doubt.

Our civilization is today reaching for the stars. And it is the technical progress made during our own lifetime that has brought them within the grasp of a generation already born.

When a society makes strides of this magnitude, it is altogether fitting that we review our progress, consider what we can learn from it, and give thought to our role in the future. As the Swiss journalist Robert Jungk has so aptly phrased it, "tomorrow is already here." It is to insure that we are prepared for the tomorrow that is already upon us that my colleagues and I concern ourselves—and it is with these problems that this book is concerned.

Part **2**

THE MANAGER'S PROBLEM

Chapter 3

THE HIGH PROMISE OF INFORMATION
TECHNOLOGY—AND FOUR PROBLEMS
IT RAISES FOR BUSINESS

*Information technology is bringing forth en-
tirely new families of machines, of which the
electronic computer is only one. Managers
must understand the nature of this phenomenon and the forces behind it if they are
properly to assess its business consequences.
The most important of the problems facing
management are seldom recognized and almost never articulated. Four of the most
basic business problems are here identified.*

This chapter is based on an address before the Council of the International Chamber of Commerce, Paris, France.

It is to the technology that we must turn to understand the business, economic, and social consequences of this new development, for it is in the technology that we find the seeds of tomorrow's world.

The heart of the technology is information theory containing new insights into the very nature of information, its communication, and its use in control—control both of inanimate objects, such as machine tools and industrial processes, and control of the organization of work in business and in government.

The business consequences of automatic data processing and electronic computers can be correctly understood only if it is appreciated that these developments are the products of a new and rapidly maturing technology.

The electronic computer is *one* early product of this technology. If this particular family of machines, in its various forms, is viewed as the entire development itself, an inaccurate picture may be formed of the business consequences and of the action necessary to utilize this technology properly.

This new technology—which I shall call information technology—is already bringing forth entirely new families of machines. Some of these machines will be of equal importance with the computer. Some may be of even greater importance.

Properly to assess the business consequences of this phenomenon, it is therefore necessary to recognize automation as a developing technology, not to view automation as a group of specific machine inventions. It is *information technology* that is important, for it is the *technology*, and the *theory* on which it is based, that will continue to yield new and radically different machines and techniques effecting as yet unexpected changes in business organizations, in our daily work, and in the very structure of society itself.

Information theory was formulated during World War II. Its origin was in the scientific research associated with the development of radar and the military systems using radar. The insights gained in this work opened to us a new world of understanding of the very nature of information.

This development is of such fundamental importance that it would be difficult indeed to overstate the magnitude of change that will take place in the lives of all of us, and in human history, as a result of the information revolution that has so unobtrusively taken place in our own day. One would be hard put to find the least evidence of popular understanding of what it means.

Information, its communication and use, is the web of society; the basis for all human understanding, organization, action, and effort. What we have gained through information theory is a better understanding of the nature of information together with a basis for the systematic—rather than the sporadic—development of means of handling information and putting it to work.

Information technology, built on the twin foundations of theory and advances in electronics, optics, and related sciences, is yielding mankind entirely new tools. And at the same time that it is extending the range of man's capabilities, it is extending also the level of his aspirations.

I have dwelt this long on what may seem a simple theoretical observation because I find that widespread lack of understanding of this most fundamental fact causes great and unnecessary problems in the practical task of putting this new technology to work.

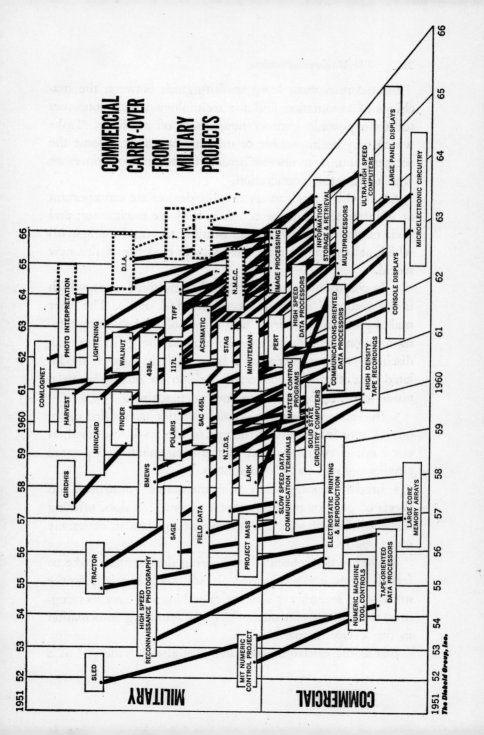

COMMERCIAL CARRY-OVER FROM MILITARY PROJECTS

The Diebold Group, Inc.

MILITARY

COMMERCIAL

SLED

TRACTOR

HIGH SPEED RECONNAISSANCE PHOTOGRAPHY

GIRDHIS

MINICARD

PHOTO INTERPRETATION

COMLOGNET

HARVEST

LIGHTENING

WALNUT

438L

TIFF

FINDER

D.I.A.

N.M.C.C.

IMAGE PROCESSING

INFORMATION STORAGE & RETRIEVAL

ULTRA-HIGH SPEED COMPUTERS

LARGE PANEL DISPLAYS

MICROELECTRONIC CIRCUITRY

MULTIPROCESSORS

117L

ACSIMATIC

STAG

MINUTEMAN

PERT

HIGH SPEED DATA PROCESSORS

COMMUNICATIONS-ORIENTED DATA PROCESSORS

CONSOLE DISPLAYS

BMEWS

POLARIS

SAC 465L

N.T.D.S.

LARK

MASTER CONTROL PROGRAMS

HIGH DENSITY TAPE RECORDINGS

SAGE

FIELD DATA

PROJECT MASS

SLOW SPEED DATA COMMUNICATION TERMINALS

SOLID STATE CIRCUITRY COMPUTERS

ELECTROSTATIC PRINTING & REPRODUCTION

HIGH SPEED RECONNAISSANCE PHOTOGRAPHY

NUMERIC MACHINE TOOL CONTROLS

LARGE CORE MEMORY ARRAYS

TAPE-ORIENTED DATA PROCESSORS

MIT NUMERIC CONTROL PROJECT

1951 52 53 54 55 56 57 58 59 1960 61 62 63 64 65 66

Businessmen must learn to distinguish between the machines of automation and the technology which continues to make possible entirely new kinds of machines. Tasks which may be impossible or uneconomic today become the accepted routine tomorrow because the technology moves on with unrelenting acceleration.

All of which is not to say that the devices are unimportant or uninteresting. On the contrary, they are fascinating; and their existence is what makes possible the machine systems which at any one time are the tangible evidence of this new world.

• In communications—the laser, a new component, which is the result of study in electronics and optics. The laser makes possible an entirely new means of long distance communication through storage of electronic energy in a crystal, discharge of that energy as a burst of light so well modulated that it can be converted back to an intelligible telephone conversation between men or machines.

• In electronic circuitry—molelectronics has yielded methods of substituting the structure of the molecule itself as electronic circuitry in place of the components and printed circuits used in today's computers.

• In data storage—thin film memories, constructed on sheets of glass or plastic as metal magnetized dots, offering the possibility of storing vast amounts of data in extremely small spaces.

These are the continually emerging devices that make us feel that tomorrow is indeed already here. But it is to the underlying technology that we must look if we are to recognize the pattern of machine systems handling information in the service of mankind.

Just as the electronic computer has already emerged as a

new product family of this technology, other entirely new families of machines will branch out from the onrushing mainstream of information technology.

• Networks of information retrieval machines—vast data stores of information automatically searched and printed out or displayed on TV screens (documents, for example, related to the indicated area of interest) will change the role of today's library as well as the mode of research.

• Teaching machines and programmed learning are already altering the most fundamental concepts of industrial training as well as the curricula of universities. Machine systems that pace the individual student, continuously analyzing his learning difficulties and mistakes and introducing remedial instruction as needed, all the while allowing direct personal participation of each individual student prohibited by classroom instruction, are today even being hailed by educators as revolutionary in impact. This development is still in its infancy.

• Language translation by machine that can scan a page, translate from one language to another, abstract the translation and then store both the abstract and the full article will materially change human communication. Based on a universal machine language of concepts and ideas, rather than direct, literal interpretation, these systems are now in the development stage.

• Medical research, today hampered by insufficient and crudely kept statistics, will surge ahead as measurements of many variables—pulse rate, temperature, blood pressure, respiration, and others—are in a form that can be manipulated for research studies as well as used to insure that a physician has a full medical history to aid in diagnosis and therapy.

• Traffic control of both air and ground vehicles has been necessary for some time if we are to keep human lives from being subject to the danger of violent death or to hours of waiting in order to travel a short distance at supersonic speed. Information technology is today making such systems possible. Air traffic control at last is being considered for one integrated international system in Europe, controlling all scheduled flights.

• Long-range weather forecasting requires the continuous collection and processing of enormous quantities of data. Earth circling systems of satellites, communication nets, and weather machines will be necessary to assemble and evaluate weather patterns on an international basis. The consequences for all human activities will be enormous, for weather throughout history has been a major determinant of social organization and development, and while it was a fellow countryman of mine who said we all talk about the weather but none of us can do anything about it, such a weather intelligence system is a first necessary step toward weather control.

These are only a sampling of the many new families of machines that will emerge from this new technology. If we adopt an even moderately long-run view of our future, these new developments can be seen as already upon us.

The technology is not yet twenty years old and already over 15,000 computers and 2,500 tape controlled machines are at work in the United States. American Telephone is planning its 1970 revenue from long distance phone calls among machines as exceeding its revenue from human city-to-city telephone calls.

Already the technology is beginning to be applied to a

wide range of problems and even today we can see the early laboratory prototypes of some of the new machines I mentioned earlier.

• One example of this is the *cybertron*, a computer which does not have to be programmed, in the usual sense of the word, to do a specific task. Rather, it goes through a learning period quite like that of a child. After the machine is taught the correct responses for certain sets of stimuli, it can give the correct responses when faced with these circumstances again. The cybertron has been taught to distinguish between real and false target echoes in sonar operations, and it compares favorably with human operators in this endeavor. It will soon be taught to evaluate data from electrocardiograms.

• Another example of the highly advanced systems which research into human processes is making possible is the *perceptron*, a pattern recognition device. The perceptron distinguishes between different letters of the alphabet and it can recognize faces and other objects.

The cybertron and perceptron are examples of the way the forms of the devices are being influenced by important developments in system knowledge.

For coupled with the many striking innovations in "hardware" are less well publicized but equally significant innovations in what we have come to call "software"—the systems and program instructions (or "packages") that are an integral and necessary part of any information system. Quite interestingly enough, the cost of software is often equal to or greater than the cost of hardware, a cost which is borne in part by the equipment manufacturer and in part by the organization employing the system.

Until recently software consisted primarily of those programs necessary to make a computer operate in a routine manner. Today much work in seemingly unrelated fields is opening to us new knowledge about information systems.

• A new breed of technologists—perhaps we can call them organization scientists—have devoted themselves to the study of behavior patterns in large human organizations, such as businesses and governments. They are studying the methods managers use in making everyday decisions. They are studying business structures, situations, and behaviors in the firm conviction that the key to the very high levels of management decision-making is the understanding and ability to simulate the process of human thought itself.

• Physiologists and neurophysiologists are studying and attempting to simulate the human environment—the adaptive behavior of the human metabolic system, neural system, and thought processes.

• Clinical and applied psychologists are studying human behavior, normal and abnormal; they are investigating human perception, conceptualization, and memory processes; and they are studying the problem-solving behavior of human beings and lower mammals.

The consequences of all these developments for business are vast. We only perceive the most crude and least important ones today:

Economies through labor saving and reductions in work force, both in factory and office.

Performance of new clerical tasks.

New statistical and accounting procedures.

Construction of performance models which project the consequences of action prior to final decision-making.

These are the standard considerations today for using computers. In a few years they will be looked back upon as the least important of the business consequences of information technology. Of greater importance will be:

• Organizational changes brought about in order better to utilize the technology and, most important of all, those brought about as a result of applying the technology.

• New businesses made possible by use of the technology both to create machines and, through machines, to render services.

The manufacture of equipment, systems, and components is a major field and a growing one.

Less obvious is the growth of new service enterprises which utilize these systems. Developments in the information retrieval field will produce new businesses; language translation will also produce new businesses. And the use of systems which perform more routine functions, such as providing nationwide hotel reservation services, is already beginning to produce new business enterprises. My own business, based on software, is in another emerging field. I have mentioned only a few of the many new businesses that have been or will be made possible through applications and developments in information technology.

Automation's greatest consequence to business, however, will be the enormous social change resulting from it. The entire role of business, its relation to human wants and its ways of satisfying those wants, depends upon society. Fundamental changes in society fundamentally change the role of business. Buying patterns, consumption habits, and other social attitudes will be radically affected by the technology and they, in turn, will produce decisive changes in business operations and business methods.

Immediate Questions

These changes—which will have the most basic and far-reaching implications for our entire business structure—are not always perceived by businessmen. When they consider the application and procedural problems that automation offers, they find many fronts of more apparent immediacy on which to focus. There are admittedly myriad pressing questions for the business executive to face. Among them are:

1. In the face of rapid change, improvement, and almost daily advances in technology, when and how does he finally make the decision to go ahead with the purchase and installation of new equipment?

2. What is the optimum investment he can make without jeopardizing his ability to meet future needs and to make future adjustments? How much of his investment now, in facilities, equipment, software, and staff, will be able to justify in the light of new developments three years, five years, ten years hence?

3. Are his cost standards and performance measures sufficiently developed to assure him of reasonable return on investment?

4. How is he to resolve conflicting recommendations from automation engineers, from his own management executives, and from equipment manufacturers?

5. How far should he attempt to coordinate the activities of his separate divisions within a machine system? How

much compatibility exists between the demands of his operating units?

Four Critical Issues

The foregoing questions undeniably pose realistic, substantive issues. But just as the layman tends to associate business automation only with manpower problems and record-keeping functions, businessmen, industrialists, and engineers overlook or fail to be aware of the most fundamental issues of all. It is imperative that we all awaken to them, for their consequences are of crucial import not only to business but to our entire economic and social structure as well.

There are four critical issues which are almost never articulated and seldom recognized. The first three discussed below are scarcely even acknowledged to be associated with the business consequences of automation.

1. *An organized discipline of information systems in business must be developed to replace the piecemeal approach that exists now.*

The systems function, when it exists at all within a business, is a collection of mixed techniques usually dealing with operations at a very low level—how many carbon copies to make, how to maintain usable cross-reference files, how to handle purchase requisitions, and the like.

Business is a complex information system, but we have yet to organize an effective approach to handling the flow of information within business. Our limitation is not attributable to the computer system, for the capability of machines has far outstripped our knowledge of how to use them to optimum advantage. What we lack is a fundamental understanding of the very business processes with which we have lived for many years. It is a truism that only when we attempt really to understand the functioning of a business system, in order to utilize most effectively our new technology, do we discover how little we know of our business operations and of ourselves. Systems discipline will ultimately come from improved understanding of control concepts and control opportunities. It will spring, too, from a more perceptive appreciation of organization and organizational relationships, of the flow of information and of how it should be used.

2. *In order to achieve an organized discipline of business-information systems fully to utilize automation technology, a new professional classification is called for in business and industry.*

The problem of building systems control requires the most thorough consideration and analysis by management. Yet management's very first rule, that authority must be commensurate with responsibility, is disregarded at almost every computer installation I am familiar with. The responsibility for incorporating technological advances, and putting them to work, is almost universally placed at too low a level, usually in a financial department, sometimes in the engineering department. Further, this responsibility tends to be associated with just one functional leg of the business and is not accepted as a company-wide service. These factors make it extraordinarily difficult to attract and hold men of the caliber to make truly great and imaginative management use of the technology. It makes it difficult for those working in the area to accomplish the magnitude of change that can and should be accomplished.

A new position must emerge within business organizations to fill this vacuum. A differentiation must be made between operating responsibilities—between the manufacturing, marketing, and planning functions. A planning function, charged with responsibility for analyzing a company's business and performing research in business information and information systems, is now beginning to become apparent at suitably high levels within some managements. It is urgent that this new function, this new profession, be recognized and developed rapidly if full use is to be made of information technology.

3. *The third basic issue is that of educating future managers in information disciplines.*

The newly emerging planning functions call for versatile, skillful, highly trained information specialists and planning executives. The International Business Machines Corporation has initiated a professional systems institute, at graduate school level, which is attempting to piece together an organized discipline for education in information systems. Industry as a whole has not yet squarely faced the problem. Universities are more keenly aware of their responsibilities to prepare for the radical changes that will occur in professional standards. A number of special courses have been created in computer and information technology at undergraduate and graduate levels. It is essential, however, for the implications of the new technology to be given greater attention in finance, production, marketing, and industrial engineering courses.

4. *The fourth great issue concerns the problem of business leadership in the social changes being created by automation.*

This issue, to which we have adverted in previous chapters, separates into two basic parts. Ironically, part of the difficulty we experience in comprehending them grows out of the fact that the consequences of one aspect have been overstated while those of the other have been understated. *Understatement* applies to the degree of change that will occur in society as a result of automation technology. None of us should harbor any doubts that the change will be very great indeed. The effects of the technological revolution we are now living through will be deeper than any social change we have experienced before.

We must identify the issue and prepare to meet it, or social change will engulf us. *Overstatement* applies to the question of manpower displacement. It is unfortunate that almost all public discussion of automation has turned on this single issue. We know little about it. Emotional reaction runs high. It gives credibility to inaccurate accounts of the human suffering that will be caused by automation.

Manpower displacement deserves much attention and study. In actual practice it is difficult, if not impossible, to determine authoritatively how much labor displacement has taken place due to automation alone. The central facts are simply that very rapid change is taking place and that we are going to have to adapt to it. It would be irresponsible for any of us to pretend that unemployment will not occur; it is even more irresponsible to assume that society is incapable of meeting such a challenge.

It is critically important that we develop a capacity and talent for leadership in this new era of technology. If we do not establish the momentum to lead society into tomorrow's world of automation, we will have no choice but to fight a retreating, defensive action that will ultimately cost us our political and economic freedoms.

Chapter 4

PRACTICAL PROBLEMS IN APPLYING INFORMATION TECHNOLOGY— FOUR STEREOTYPES TO QUESTION

Automation has presented management with a major new problem. As yet management has not faced up to this problem; in fact is not even grappling with it in any true sense. There is a wide gulf between the possession of the marvelous new machines and their profitable use. Management must learn to use the new technology to gain more accurate and timely information about the operation of a business, and to capitalize on such information through new decision-making techniques. This can now be done in ways that were impossible before the advent of information technology. But managers will have to look afresh at each development and overcome certain stereotypes, myths, and limita-

tions. They will also have to exercise genuine control over the new information systems in terms of objectives, costs, and results.

This chapter is based upon an address presented before the IV International Management Congress, CIOS, Paris, France.

Management has not yet dealt in a comprehensive way with the consequences of advanced information technology. This is through no lack of energy or good intentions. On the contrary, the very activity of management in this sphere attests to the progressive spirit and desire for improvement that characterize the modern manager. The trouble lies elsewhere. Automation has turned out to be a much more complex and difficult problem than was originally thought. This being the case, the current disposition to minimize its revolutionary and novel aspects is more hindrance than help in putting automation to work.

Despite a lively readiness to buy the machines of automation, management is doing all too little hard thinking about how to use them. This is the real crux of the dilemma we find ourselves in today and it is a difficult problem.

It is the exception rather than the rule to find genuine personal concern on the part of a top level manager with his automation program. Ordering the machines all too often seems to be a way of appeasing management's conscience that something is really being done about an important but unknown new field. By and large, managements are accepting the generalities they hear about automation. The unfortunate part about it is that too few of the published accounts are based on practical experience. The danger, it has been well said, is not in having push-button machines, but in being content with a "push-button type of thinking."

There is an almost incredible preoccupation with equipment. Yet the hard truth of the matter is that we have hardly begun to learn how to put these splendid new machines to work.

In dealing with automation most managements have exhibited a degree of credulity unthinkable in other aspects of business. Few managements are even yet consciously seeking performance standards with which to measure the real progress of the automation programs upon which they have embarked. It may be the laxity of economic boom, uncertainty in dealing with this new and highly technical field, or the difficulty of coping with such a radical departure from conventional procedures (operation in areas where there are as yet no bench marks to which management can look for guidance). Whatever the reason, businessmen are simply not treating the time, money, and talent they are investing in automation with anything like the hard, rigorous analysis one should expect where the stakes, both in terms of investment and potential, are so high. Admittedly, much must be written off to research and education—to learning the ropes of this new field—but a great deal more is being chalked up to the "education" account than should properly be placed there.

Automation, as a word and as a fact, is only about fifteen years old. Surprising as it may seem, even in this new field, most management thinking has already become rigid and cluttered with stereotypes that stand in the way of real progress. New insights are needed. It is up to management to do a good deal more original thinking and to learn to question traditional patterns of operation.

Virtually everything that is said or written about automation stresses the machines. Certainly these devices are fascinating. Indeed, it is their very complexity and their technological splendor that deceive us into thinking we have made more progress than we really have. But it is dead wrong to equate the bewildering array of hardware shipments of recent years with true progress in the use of automation.

A striking fact about management's attitude toward automation is its failure to realize that there is a wide gulf between the possession of the machines and the profitable use of these powerful new tools. What is needed to cover this gulf is a great deal of work by a management that has foresight into what automation really is and how it can be used. But first must come a realization that "taking the plunge" of acquiring machinery does not automatically open the magic gates to the world of tomorrow.

The sight of magnetic tape computers operating in business offices is commonplace in the United States. Many people, including most of the managements of the companies possessing these computers, think they are using automation, or feel that they are at least well on the way to reaping its benefits. The real facts, once unearthed, are in striking contrast. Few of the business organizations that use computers are doing anything more with them than they did perfectly adequately before by less elaborate methods. Many are doing it at considerably greater cost.

It is proper to raise the question of whether or not the long lead time that even the best automation programs require before results can be expected has not often been taken advantage of to postpone the day of reckoning for programs that simply will never pay out. The high turnover rate and excessive job hopping that characterize this field certainly play their part in obscuring the real facts from management.

It may come as an unpleasant surprise when I say that I do not believe management is facing up to the problem of

automation, especially if one has spent time and money trying to apply the benefits of automation to office or factory.
A good deal of time is spent in discussion of conflicting
definitions of what automation "really" is. There is much
truth in the quip that it is as hard for a group of businessmen to define automation as it is for a group of theologians
to define sin.

One's capacity for wonder would be dull indeed if it
were not stirred by stories of gigantic oil refineries centrally
controlled from a single instrument room with the help of
only a few men, or of the giant computers that can count
and calculate in fractions of a second, or of the famous
transfer machines of Ford, Renault, and Austin that automatically machine a cylinder block from a rough casting in
less than fifteen minutes. *Nonetheless, by stressing the
achievements of these remarkable devices, the definitions
have obscured the real essential of automation: that it is,
more than anything else, a concept or a way of approach
in solving problems, and that it marks a considerable departure from many accepted practices of management.*

In my opinion, almost all the defining and counter-
defining misses the point and misses it in a very serious way.
In a sense, the definitions themselves are to a considerable
degree actually responsible for the misconceptions about automation that are causing many managements to miss the
point, to put the emphasis in the wrong place, and to lose
out on most of the benefits that automation could bring.

It is not that the new technology is unimportant. On the
contrary, without these self-correcting machines most of
what is considered to be automation by any definition simply
could not exist. But the importance of the machines does

not lie in their ability to perform mechanical tricks. They are important because, for the first time, they enable us to organize many different kinds of business operations, in the office and in the plant, into systems, and to control these systems far more precisely than ever before. More than this, they enable us to do new things, as well as to perform old tasks better.

Automation is not a particular group of new machines or devices. It is a new concept—the idea of self-regulating systems—and a new set of principles. Only when management understands this will it gain the full benefit from automation, but this kind of understanding is still so rare as to be almost an isolated phenomenon in the business world.

Some Automation Myths

I have mentioned certain stereotypes of automation that block effective management thinking. I would now like to give examples of what I mean. Every one of these stereotypes has some truth in it; that is undoubtedly why they persist. Yet so long as they are swallowed whole, just so long will automation fail to mean what it could mean in the factory, the processing plant, and the office. These stereotypes are in large part the result of accepting the common view that automation consists of specific automatic machines. Among the most important of them are:

1. That automation is primarily useful as a labor-saving device.
2. That the ultimate in automation can be symbolized by an oil refinery or any other highly instrumented process plant.
3. That because automation is highly technical most of

the decisions concerning it must be left to the engineers and technicians.

4. That only companies with large dollar resources and exceptionally long runs of product can afford to automate.

Stereotype 1: That automation is primarily useful as a labor-saving device.

This stereotype is especially pernicious because, at first glance, it seems so plausible. For office management in particular, both clerical costs and the difficulty of hiring enough clerks to get the work done are serious problems. Consider these facts for a moment. Between 1920 and 1950, the number of United States factory workers increased by 53 per cent, but the number of office workers increased 150 per cent. Today there are almost twice as many office workers as there were in 1940. One insurance company that installed a computer to handle some of its office procedures had been plagued with recurrent shortages of clerical labor for fifteen years. Small wonder that automatic data processing equipment is often looked on as the answer to a management nightmare.

And the fact is that the machinery of automation in most cases probably will make some dent on this problem. Savings in this area have led a lot of management thinking to run this way: "If we buy a computer and let it handle, say, payroll, it will soon pay for itself because we can cut way down on staff and on punched card machines. Then, after it has the payroll under its belt, we can begin to let it solve some of those big intangible problems that you can't even put a dollar value on."

The trouble with this kind of thinking is that it overlooks the remarkable potentialities of these machines for doing what cannot be done at all without them. Payroll, after all, can be handled perfectly adequately by punched card machines; the pay checks come out on time and they are accurate, even though the job may take the time of a great many clerks. Putting routine operations on a computer may pay for the computer in the end, but it can rarely do a great deal more than that.

Executives will never realize the potential of the new equipment if they persist in thinking of automatic data processing in terms of merely eliminating a few, or even a good many, employees by speeding up old procedures and routines. Mechanization of existing procedures may merely result in compounding and perpetuating inefficiency. The real aim is not to speed up an old job but to do a better job. Part of the challenge of automation to management is learning to use new tools to solve new as well as old problems.

The big benefits from automatic data processing will come only when management learns to use automation for its unique ability to provide better, more accurate, and more timely information about the operation of a business.

The thought of more information is a frightening one for the executive who knows that his desk and briefcase are already bulging with information that he has not even had time to read, let alone digest. When my firm analyzed the operations of a large publishing company, we found that the president received 621 reports during a three-month period, more than one every working hour. And, as W. W. Smith of General Electric has pointed out, "The mass of reports management receives today may be likened to a daily newspaper printed without headlines and without punctuation, without spacing between lines and words, and without capital letters. The mental gymnastics required to determine exactly what is going on is asking too much."

But management, if it uses the new tools correctly, will soon find that what it has now is not really too much information but not enough of the right kind, because the mass of data is too great to be processed by conventional equipment. We will be able to do two kinds of things that we cannot now do at all or can only do in a rudimentary manner.

First, we will be able to plan in advance on the basis not of guesses and hopes but of facts, because automatic data processing can give realistic answers to "what would happen if . . ." questions.

A major domestic United States airline asked one of these questions when it put maintenance scheduling on a computer. Whenever a plane breaks down, an airline has a complicated rescheduling problem with literally thousands of possible solutions. In effect, the airline asked a computer about each flight on its schedule: "What would happen if this flight should break down tomorrow? What is the best way to use our other planes while that one is being repaired?" The computer was able to run through all possible solutions in a half hour and to pick the best one in each case. As a result, this particular airline saved one standby Constellation in each of six airports at a saving, for each plane, of one million dollars a year in lost revenue. With jet planes, the comparable saving will be five million dollars a year for each plane. In many areas of business today we must make decisions based on incomplete information, and so "fly by the seat of our pants," as we say in the States. For example, recalculating complicated budgets or schedules to determine ahead of time the precise effect of a certain decision is too great and too long a task to be practical except when the decision is a major one. Automation gives us tools to practice this type of "what would happen if" management, allowing us to build models of alternative solutions, and so gives us quantitative answers about the effects of contemplated policy changes. Thus, in the example above, the airline was able to experiment on paper—or more exactly, on magnetic tape—and to predict the consequences of alternative procedures.

Second, management will be able to get quick, complete answers to problems whose solutions now are incomplete and often arrive too late to be of great use.

Recently, a major publishing company was forced to discontinue two of its publications, both widely circulated and historically important magazines. There were many complicated reasons why this action was necessary, but here is a case where the use of automation for decision-making might have prevented the final disaster. Because of difficult financial conditions, it was known before the discontinuance of the two magazines that the publication of a third company magazine might be terminated and its resources and circulation thrown behind the other two. It was necessary to determine what proportion of the circulation of this magazine duplicated subscription to either one or both of the other two magazines.

Circulation records were kept on punched cards, but they were of such volume that a cross check of the entire three lists was too expensive. Unfortunately, the sample that was taken proved imprecise and the company underestimated the number of "cross subscriptions." The result was that the company experienced a severe and unexpected cash drain in securing enough new subscriptions to meet the circulation guarantee. This set off a series of chain reactions at a critical moment. All three magazines were finally discontinued.

Although such a serious error in decision-making need not be fatal in a strong business situation, it was in this case. And this case was one where advanced automatic data processing could have been used to make the necessary calculations before the final decision, and possibly have averted the collapse of the magazines.

When automatic data processing is used in this way, it can turn the present art of management into a real science of management. It thus becomes clear that management which puts labor saving first has its eye on the wrong ball. More efficient operation and better control are the real goals. If labor is saved as a by-product, so much the better.

Stereotype 2: That the ultimate in automated machinery has been realized by oil refineries and other highly instrumented process plants.

An oil refinery where instruments and controls far outnumber the human workers gives the impression of being a very highly automated operation. Compared with an automobile factory or other metal fabricating facility, it is. Yet nothing could be further from the truth than to say, as one business magazine did, that "the men have to be there anyway in case of emergency, so the extra costs of more instruments to read other instruments is not considered justified at this time." This is just one more example of a statement that misses the whole implication of this technological revolution to business.

Refineries have achieved what fabricating is still struggling for—a conversion from batch to continuous processing so that operation can be made automatic. However, they are only beginning to feel the full impact of a second, and more significant, stage when the automatic operations will be automatically controlled.

The intricate controls that run a refinery *almost* by themselves are in a large sense not really running it at all. As things stand, the variables of processing—temperature, pressure, level and rate of flow—can be maintained at desired values without human intervention through the use of feedback control devices. The values themselves must still be selected by human beings and the control instruments adjusted accordingly. In many cases, it is not possible to determine the relationships among these variables that will hold true throughout an entire process. This means that an operator cannot come to work, set his controls, and go home. He must reset them every time a test of the product being processed shows that changes are needed.

Thus it is the operator who does all the decision-making. Since a refinery is an extremely complex operation, it is more a matter of luck than of science when he makes the best possible decision on each of the variables at any given moment. The result is that even such a highly automated industry as refining works most of the time on a trial-and-error basis. The best refinery—to judge from some tests that have recently been run using the instrument records of several first-rate refineries—probably does not operate at optimum for more than a few minutes out of the entire 24-hour operating day! The rest of the time output is fluctuating around, and sometimes quite far from, optimum. Genuinely effective control, it is estimated, could increase yields by as much as 30 per cent.

For dealing with a process that allows blending to achieve

an acceptable final product, as is the case with petroleum refining and the manufacture of many chemicals, control such as this may be adequate. However, in manufacturing some of the new complex synthetics, such as dacron for example, it is another story. It is impossible to make up for sloppy controls by blending, because the product is either right or it is not: there is no in-between that can be corrected by adding a little something extra at the end. Such processes require that an exquisite level of control be maintained among many rapidly fluctuating variables, and the *only* way it can be done is by use of a highly complex overall control system. The lack of such control equipment today results in a great deal of the output of such plants going into waste, and this waste is reflected in the cost of the end products.

To achieve genuinely effective process plan control, all the plant's individual controls will have to be integrated into a single, coordinated, *self-regulating* system. Just as a single machine designed on the feedback principle notes and corrects variations in its output, so an integrated self-regulating system will note and correct variations in the end-product of an *entire plant* and make precise and instantaneous adjustments whenever the product itself shows any variation from optimum quality. Since the control of a number of variables to produce a desired end is essentially a calculating operation, the integrated operation of the process plant of the future will depend upon an electronic computer to analyze, correlate, and correct the operations of the individual control devices.

There are two reasons why no processing plant is using a computer in this way. There is, as yet, no computer that is reliable enough to operate suitably in an "on line" capacity for long periods of time, although manufacturers are very close to achieving one. More serious, however, is the fact that scientists simply do not know enough about how process variables affect each other and the end product. To date, there are no instruments that can measure reliably, accurately, swiftly, and continuously all the variables of refinery operation, and no engineer who can measure, relate, and reduce to equations that a computer can handle all the process conditions that determine the quality of a given end product.

Today automatic logging devices, specifically in the form of automatic typewriters, can print out in sequence the reading from each instrument. Readings that represent variations greater than normal are typed in red, and a machine can be programmed so that it will index, skip to the bottom of the log sheet, type the off-normal reading in red, and get back to its business on the upper half of the log sheet. The machine puts on quite a show for the engineers who have been alerted by sight and sound alarms.

It was only a short and obvious second step to attach a paper tape punch to the automatic typewriter. Instrument readings are thus made automatically and are quickly available in a form that can be processed through a calculating device which will actually perform the engineering calculations of yield in a refinery.

Thus far,* however, equipment has not been developed for the completely automatic control which will be achieved when each of the regulating instruments can automatically correct alterations in the variable it measures in terms of

* Note: As of June, 1957.

changes in all other related variables. Nonetheless, it is an important step to be able to derive accounting and production data directly from the process itself, thereby eliminating the costs, the delay, the inevitable error, and the boredom of manual recording, recopying, and eventually keying information into an office machine for subsequent reprocessing. Once it is possible not only automatically to scan and record variables, but to compute the best course of adjusting them, the feedback loop will be closed, and the entire process can be controlled in terms of changes in the characteristics of the end product. When this *end-point control* has been brought about, management will have a far higher level of control over the process, and the "marriage" of plant and office will be even more complete. Management will then be able to use its facilities to produce increased yields of better products at lower cost.

Stereotype 3: That since new complex machinery is highly technical most of the decisions concerning it must be left to engineers and technicians.

This new machinery is indeed extremely complex. The science of communication and control, on which it is based, is easily among the half dozen most advanced frontiers of technology, and the computer is the most advanced piece of equipment yet built in this field.

However, no one is asking management to build a computer or to repair one if it breaks down. Those are jobs that only technicians can do. But management, too, has a unique function and one that is, in its way, as complex and difficult. Perhaps more so. Truly fruitful results from information handling systems require a fundamental change in approach, an understanding that the best applications come not from

SYSTEM EVOLUTION

1954

COST DISTRIBUTION

75%	CENTRAL PROCESSOR
15%	INPUT-OUTPUT
10%	DIGITAL FILES
0%	IMAGE FILES
0%	COMMUNICATIONS

SPEED: 1000 OPERATIONS/SECOND
CAPACITY: 40,000 CHARACTERS

DIEBOLD GROUP ESTIMATES

1963

COST DISTRIBUTION

60%	CENTRAL PROCESSOR
15%	INPUT-OUTPUT
15%	DIGITAL FILES
0%	IMAGE FILES
10%	COMMUNICATIONS

SPEED: 150,000 OPERATIONS/SECOND
CAPACITY: 200,000 CHARACTERS

1972

COST DISTRIBUTION

25%	CENTRAL PROCESSOR
25%	INPUT-OUTPUT
20%	DIGITAL FILES
15%	IMAGE FILES
15%	COMMUNICA-TIONS

SPEED: 4,000,000 OPERATIONS/SECOND
CAPACITY: 15,000,000 CHARACTERS

The Diebold Group, Inc.

the mechanization or streamlining of existing procedures, but are based on management's willingness to rethink the problems of an *entire business* in terms of ultimate goal and final product. These are not technical problems. They are problems of definition of objectives and assessments of markets, of method, organization, and attitude. They require managerial imagination, skill, and experience to solve them, rather than mere technical proficiency.

Bluntly stated, automation is one of the critical areas in which management must *manage*. Instead of realizing this crucial point, management has become so intimidated by the complexity of new hardware that it has allowed technicians to take over not only the operation of the machines but the actual decisions about how they are to be used. This has led to a whole series of difficulties.

For one thing, there is the electronics committee. Time after time, executives answer the question, "What are you doing about automation?" with: "We have formed an electronics committee." They imply that the problem has thus been taken care of. In practice, this often means that the committee spends a year—or in one documented case, three years—wandering about the country, attending manufacturers' schools, and visiting computer installations. This experience is somehow supposed to be sufficient for making critical decisions about the highly detailed process of automating the company's information network.

The electronics committee has often been a device for creating the impression of doing something while at the same time avoiding any action that could possibly backfire. Many managements genuinely seem to be looking at this subject as if they were walking around the edge of an ice-cold swimming pool. They realize that sooner or later they are going to have to jump in, but they try to postpone the leap with as much rationalization and fact-gathering as possible. In one case, the electronics committee of a major oil company, after a year's study, actually presented the final equipment choice to the president of the company by asking him to choose between the machines of two different manufacturers.

The installation of information handling equipment should not be made unless it is based on a thorough understanding of the business itself, and the functions and needs of its operations. Most engineers underestimate both the importance of this point and the difficulties of grasping the complexity of modern business operations. Ironically, while the businessman may regard the specialized knowledge of the engineer with something approaching awe, the engineer frequently regards the unfamiliar processes of business as something that can be mastered in a few months. Glenn White of the Chrysler Corporation has remarked out of the experience of his company that "we are satisfied that the way to put together a team of people to work on electronics is to take somebody who has good knowledge of how to run your business, a good systems and procedures man, if you please. They can be trained in electronics much easier than somebody who knows electronics can be trained in how to run your business."

Stereotype 4: That only companies with large dollar resources and exceptionally long runs of product can afford to take advantage of new automated and information handling equipment.

This is not wholly true today and before long it will be

even less true. However, the reason the impression has arisen is easy to understand.

The automobile industry, an automation pioneer, has had great success with very expensive and very specialized industrial equipment made for the requirements of a particular product. The large transfer machine, complete with loading and unloading devices, is well suited for this industry where literally millions of identical parts pass through a line before new equipment has to be considered.

Such machines are not so well suited to the estimated 80 per cent of American industry that produces in lots of twenty-five or fewer identical pieces. Nor are they well suited for industries that frequently redesign their products, since any major change in design means costly readjustments at best and may even mean scrapping this expensive machinery. However, advanced technology dealing with feedback and control systems is producing a new family of machines guided by magnetic or punched paper tape. These machines make it possible to obtain the benefits of automatic production, yet retain the flexibility of operation essential for job shop production. These numerical control devices are making their impact felt. Some forty different prototypes can be found in the shops of machine tool manufacturers and during the next few years* they will have an increasing effect on the small lot producers of this country.

Management that uses the excuse of small lots to avoid the issues of advanced technology may well be guilty of the fallacy of "job shop thinking." For example, one of the largest manufacturers of shovels in the world wanted to automate production. His plant produced hundreds of dif-

---

* Note: The time is June, 1957.

ferent kinds of special-purpose shovels in small lots. Each kind, since its shape is unique, was being produced separately. The whole factory was nothing more than a collection of job shops under one roof. Yet analysis showed that about 80 per cent of the company's production was limited to not much more than a dozen different models and that this bulk of the plant's total production could be made automatic without great difficulty.

The most basic thinking about automation had not yet been done in this plant. Their problem was not simply a question of buying new machines, but of reorganizing the old machines and the old procedures in a more systematic, more productive way. Although reorganizing existing equipment may go no further than introducing good principles of materials flow, it is an essential first step in integrating the fabricating operation, prior to linking the individual machines, just as such integration must precede the introduction of overall automatic control.

STEPS IN THE RIGHT DIRECTION

It is of utmost importance that management exorcise these stereotypes from its thinking. But getting rid of false ideas is only the first step. The next steps are positive ones: to understand the factors that make for a successful program of integrating new automatic machines and information handling equipment into a company program, and then to apply them.

There are four essential steps management must take for a successful program. It must:

1. Define the objectives of the program
2. Staff it carefully

3. Estimate costs realistically
4. Train personnel

1. *Defining Objectives*

What does management want these new machines to accomplish? This question cannot possibly be answered without a thorough preliminary systems study that will define the problems to be dealt with and determine how the organization can best go about handling them.

First of all, there is no point in automating at all simply for the sake of automating. It is a rare executive who will admit that his company is investigating this field simply because his golf partner's company has already installed equipment, or because he has been overwhelmed by glamorous advertisements and newspaper stories. Nonetheless, there are reasons to believe that at least as many supposedly hardheaded businessmen have bought expensive equipment on this basis—and lived to be disappointed in it—as there are businessmen who have gone through the practical, painstaking, and time-consuming process of a thorough analysis of the *entire organization as an integrated system*, including office operations and marketing.

Management that has taken this indispensable preliminary step will never make the mistake of confusing the tangible possession of the hardware with the practical use of the concept. Nor will it commit the fallacy of the "step by step" approach. The statement that "we are taking a step by step approach to automation" conveys the impression of caution and proper business reserve. What it often means in fact is that another uncoordinated misstep is being taken. While caution is a desirable thing, what is so misleading about this approach is that the whole concept of systems analysis and design requires a careful and detailed plan for the entire organization if the benefits realized are to be more than marginal. Following a step by step approach often results in throwing out the previous step and redoing a great amount of work to install the procedures and equipment associated with the new steps. This approach is also likely to mean mechanizing old procedures one step at a time, instead of finding out whether some of these procedures are not outmoded altogether.

A thorough analysis will prevent the management of medium-sized concerns from falling into the trap of trying to use the same approach as that of very large companies. A company like Du Pont, for example, can afford to buy a computer and experiment with it on a single application or a series of separate applications. And in many giant organizations, enough people are involved in a single process like payroll or billing so that at least a superficial case can be made for mechanizing this one job, if for no other reason than that the company is gaining experience in computer use. On the other hand, the data processing activities of smaller firms are typified not by their routineness but by their variety and interconnection. To lift one department arbitrarily from this interconnected whole for the sake of speeding up its routine processes will never lead to the ultimate goal—the design of the information processing system best suited to the particular requirements of the individual organization.

It is often necessary to *rethink* an entire operation in order to define the objectives of the program. Sometimes what management believes to be the problems are in reality symptoms, and the true problems lie far deeper. It is important not to automate in order to tackle symptoms. A thorough systems analysis and a careful thinking through of objectives is the best means of defining the true problem. At the same time an adequate systems study can save management from the opposite but equally serious mistake of trying to make too fundamental a change in one pass.

Similarly, it is often necessary to redesign the product, or the process, or both, in order to make the introduction of new technology feasible. In stating objectives, a company must be careful not to "define itself" out of automation altogether. For example, in designing a highly automated plant for the manufacture of telephones, the problem faced was the automating of the manufacture and assembly of some intricate electrical circuitry. If the task had been defined in terms of assembling the product as it had been designed for hand assembly, the equipment investment would have been prohibitive. By defining the objective as creating a network circuit that could function just as the old one did, it was possible to redesign the equipment in such a way that automation proved feasible.

2. *Staffing the Program*

It is not enough to realize that such a program is best run by choosing a man who understands the business, rather than by an engineer who understands automated equipment. It is of crucial importance to choose the *very best man the company can find* to head the program.

Most top managements are appalled to learn that they will not only have to put a key person in charge of the program but that he will have to spend as much as a year simply studying the problems and learning how to solve them. "Why, I can't spare my best man," executives have said, "I have to keep the business running, don't I?" Nonetheless, it is false economy to do anything else.

Consider what the responsibility means for a full scale program of automation and integration of the corporation's information network: It means a thorough study of the entire business and a well-grounded understanding of its aims and goals. It involves responsibility for making a detailed systems analysis. While it does not necessarily involve intimate knowledge of the technical details of equipment, it involves something much more important—knowledge of what machines are available, their advantages and disadvantages, their potentials and limitations—so that the equipment finally purchased will be the equipment that best fits the needs of the system. It involves responsibility for setting up a training program within the organization for those who will actually be using the equipment, and an orientation program for those whose operations will be affected by it. Finally, it involves running the program itself once the equipment is installed.

To give this responsibility to a superannuated vice-president, simply because he can easily be spared from present operations, is practically to guarantee at least partial failure for the program before it starts.

3. *Estimating Costs*

One important reason that hoped-for savings from automation have often failed to materialize is that management has not always been realistic about costs. Businessmen considering such a program tend to make two mistakes. They count the cost of the machinery itself, but they do not recognize the associated, often hidden, costs of using it; and they base their plans for the equipment on the assumption that its cost must be justified by immediate and obvious savings. Since a reduction in labor costs is the most immediate and obvious saving, this consideration becomes the justification for buying the equipment, and then dominates its use after it has been installed. In the process, the possibility of capital savings so substantial as to dwarf any conceivable gains from labor savings is overlooked altogether.

The paper-making machine is a case in point. The introduction of an automatic control system on the city-block-long equipment is not likely to remove a single man from the payroll, since many men will be needed to handle breaks in the paper and to run the new equipment. Yet the new system may allow an increase in the speed of the equipment from, say, 2,000 feet per minute to 2,500 feet per minute. The increase in productivity of the equipment, which represents a capital investment of $10 million to $15 million, results in a sizable decrease in the capital cost per unit of useful product.

Similarly, the economics of computer installations are incompletely understood. Management often does not realize that the cost of installing a computer and converting existing procedures will approach the cost of the computer itself. Briefly, this means that if a company is planning to spend a million dollars for a computer, it had better count on spending an additional million dollars for planning, installation, and conversion costs. These may not all appear in the direct cost breakdowns associated with the computer, but they are very likely to be real costs borne by the organization in assimilating the change. If management fails to take this into account there is bound to be disappointment in the length of time that it takes the computer to pay for itself.

It is also important to understand that once the system is in, the largest expense will be the cost of preparing data for the machines. If additional useful information can be extracted as a by-product of something the computer is doing anyway, the economics may be enormously changed. That is why the payroll is seldom the best way to use a computer. To put it on the computer in the first place is complex and time consuming, and once it is on there is no easy way for management to get additional useful data from this application, unless it has been planned as part of a system having several objectives beyond payroll preparation alone.

4. *Training Personnel*

Just as important as recognizing the need for the right man to head the automation program is the realization that personnel to run the program do not necessarily have to be hired from outside the organization. In fact, there are excellent reasons for training a company's own personnel rather than attempting to bring automation specialists into the organization.

The training of personnel in analytical procedures, machine operations, and programming is one of the most critical problems of a successful automation installation. It involves good insight into how to select, train, and retrain already employed personnel to work with the new equipment and the new procedures. To go far afield to find help only complicates matters further. The mad quest for skilled scientific personnel that is currently taking place in the United States has brought into existence a large group of "job floaters" who are unstable and often disruptive in an organization when they are introduced over the protests of personnel people.

One cause of the personnel problem is that hardware is

being shipped faster than competent people have been trained to operate it. The answer is not to go into the job market for specialists. Good ones are exceptionally hard to find, and money is no longer an incentive for the already highly paid experienced man. These men are looking for very specialized kinds of opportunities. The solution is to train personnel from within.

Fundamental to the success of a program to incorporate information technology into a company is the clear-cut indication by management that the program is its direct concern. It must be clear that management is willing to do the hard work involved in carrying out its responsibility, and that it intends to exercise real control over the program —its objectives, its costs, and its results.

Chapter 5

EDUCATING MANAGERS FOR CHANGE—
A BUSINESS RESPONSIBILITY

The central problem of automation is the problem of education on every level—technical, managerial, and general. Improved education for tomorrow's managers, and intensive retraining of today's, is imperative if we are to achieve maximum utilization of the tools science and technology provide. The immediate major training effort must be performed by business itself. No other institutions are as adequately equipped to do the job. And this training must not be confined to the limited area of specific machine applications. It must be broad in scope and imaginative. The task is not to train technicians, but to educate managers. The educated manager of the future will be the man who has been educated to adapt to change.

This chapter is based on a Great Issues Lecture delivered at Dartmouth College, Hanover, New Hampshire.

The great issues of the world can often be narrowed to a single point. This is certainly true in the case with automation. The machines, and the problems they pose for management, are enormously complex, but one problem emerges as basic. That problem is education. Successful transition to the new era beyond automation will call for educational innovation at several levels.

For example, a world where everyone experiences increasing leisure will place a demand on educational institutions to provide people with the cultural backgrounds that will enable them to enrich their lives by proper use of the new leisure. And a world subject to the rapid changes we have envisioned will call for education on a continuing basis, long after graduation. Six year olds now starting school can expect their vocations to change three times during their lifetimes. One shot of formal education may have sufficed for their parents, but this new generation will need some form of education all during life.

Finally, a whole new approach to business management will require retraining and expanded education for business executives. A world of accelerating change requires that educators not merely *train technicians*, but also *educate men* who can adapt to change.

Change is replacing the traditional foundation of our business organization, division of labor, with the new concept of the integrated system. Change of this magnitude is not going to be brought about by leasing a computer and then sending ten or twenty people to programming school to learn how to operate it. These changes are basic to the way business is organized and operated.

The need to make these changes presents business management with the most colossal job of education ever faced. The need is here today. There is no choice but to meet it, and to do so at once. The men and women already in business are the ones who must bring about these changes. They must be adequately trained for the task, and for the present at least this gigantic training effort must be performed by business itself. There is no other institution able to do the job.

Today there are large numbers of splendid new machines as technically complex and powerful as any that man has ever produced. The facts reveal, however, that extremely few of these machines are being used in a way that even begins to exploit their full potential. The reason for this is the lack of proper knowledge of how to use them efficiently, and little understanding at all of how to use them to solve management problems. Consequently, there is an urgent need for basic education in training the men and women in business—not just in how to work the machines, but in the far more difficult task of how to employ them properly and profitably.

The machines are only symbols of fundamental developments that are taking place in the way work is organized. The training of management personnel must reflect this fact. However, the educational programs that have accompanied this new technology do not begin to reflect this fact because the businessmen who understand this are themselves very rare.

At the start, and for quite a few more years, the practical solution to the problem of retraining management properly to utilize the new technology is going to have to come from business itself. There is no hope in the immediate future that the buck can be passed along to the colleges and high schools. In time, if business truly understands what its needs are, and makes these needs known, the educational system will begin to produce young men and women trained not just to use automation equipment but to understand its potentials.

As things now stand, the great bulk of the people who must accomplish the crucial task of administering the conversion of business to new information systems, and those who are going to be living and working in a world at least partly automated, are men and women who have already completed their formal education and are now working in business and industry. The responsibility for training these people is largely that of private business, and the task is a far larger one than most managements as yet realize.

Current attempts at training in data processing depend largely on the courses in how to use the machines that equipment manufacturers give to their customers' personnel, and on a few similar university extension programs. Such training is almost always tied to machines, and it is hardly adequate even to develop a proper understanding of the machines. It rarely begins to indicate the problem of how to apply them. Moreover, these schools are tied not only to machines, which is bad enough, but to the machines of one particular manufacturer. Attending only one of these schools is something like expecting to learn all about political science by spending a few weeks in the local Republican or Democratic headquarters.

What is needed is training that is more basic, broader in scope, more intensive, and given in greater depth. For example, the success of a computer installation depends only partly on adequate technical training in programming for those who will actually convert a given business task to machine instructions. Even this is a training problem that, in itself, requires many months of on-the-job instruction beyond the scant month or two in a manufacturer's school if a prudent businessman is to feel confident that the success or failure of the entire program is not just a gamble. A successful computer installation depends even more on training in depth of the many individuals within the organization who are not directly involved in any way with the machine or its operation.

The sales manager of a company, for example, must understand a good deal about what a computer can do if he is even to begin to take advantage of its powerful potential for producing new kinds of market and distribution analysis. It is the sales manager, not the head of the data processing center, who knows what sales information is critical. The computer expert can only present what he thinks the sales manager needs. This is equally true of production control, cost accounting, and financial accounting—indeed, of virtually all areas of business management.

Education in breadth as well as in depth is needed, if top management is to know how to specify its requirements and if middle management is to understand how to structure its problems, what kinds of data to gather, and how to analyze them. One reason why business computers have not produced better results is that new reports and analyses have almost always been produced—and have had to be produced —by the computer people; executives have not known enough about the computer's potential to phrase their own information specifications in any but the most general terms.

Once an organized discipline of systems design exists, a

formal educational program can be established. Until that time—still some years off—our best efforts will be little more than makeshift. (Thus far, the most serious effort at such an educational program is a graduate-level, internal school called Systems Research Institute, conducted by the International Business Machines Corporation.)

The task faced by the businessman is to bridge this gap between business problems and scientific solutions and to administer research efforts that are basic in character. It is no easy problem. Russian space accomplishments are proof both of the rewards of the scientific approach and the dangers of applying old-fashioned business management to a research effort. The task of finding new methods of administering and guiding basic research in business is as difficult as it is pressing.

The immediate educational burden imposed by automation is one that must be solved largely in the gray flannel world of Cash McCall and Willis Wayde. But it does not end there. Business, of course, cannot be expected to shoulder the long term educational problem alone. In the long run, it must depend on the high schools and colleges to do the job for which they were established. Even then, it is the responsibility of business to make clear its real needs. Its influence can be important, perhaps crucial, in determining what kind of education will be offered.

The most important requirement of the new education is high quality. There is much talk about the current shortage of engineers. Every year this nation falls some thousands short of the number needed: by 1970, according to the U.S. Department of Labor, we will require over one million more scientists and engineers than we had in 1960. The average annual demand over this ten year period comes to 71,700 engineers and 29,500 scientists for each respective year from 1960 to 1970.

In the age of automation and of other complex new technical developments, Professor Gordon S. Brown of M.I.T. has pointed out, "Those electrical engineers who learned only to go to the handbook for recipes having to do with generators, transmission lines, or telephones are not prepared to cope with new developments, much less to contribute to them. . . . We believe we should prepare students not only for electrical engineering as it exists today but to play a creative role in and to lead the electrical engineering of tomorrow."

It is a healthy sign that business, too, is coming to recognize that narrowly specialized training is precisely the wrong kind of training for the men who will be expected to play a creative role in designing and building machines for this new technical age. "Teach your students the basic principles which will never change," one industrialist has urged. "Don't teach them current engineering practice. If you teach them current practice, the chances are that it will not be the practice of my company, and if it is, the practice will be obsolete before the students can use it." One real contribution businessmen can make is not only to support but to spread this point of view.

Beyond this, there is an even larger educational problem that affects everyone. Despite all that has been said about how the new technology is narrowing man's role, everything indicates that there will be an increasing importance and a greater role for the individual. One thing appears certain: *automation is going to demand far better educated men, in the fullest sense of the word.* Many of the new jobs that are being created will require an increasing ability to think and to judge, increased understanding of mathematical and logical methods—in short, increased education in the largest sense of the term.

The easiest mistake one can make, and certainly the most common, is to assume that scientific training must be the root of all education in the future, and that only those trained as scientists will play important roles. This is a mistake not because technology is unimportant, but because what is truly important, both for technology and for society as a whole, is orderly thinking, and orderly thinking is neither necessarily nor exclusively developed by studying science.

Automation, and other technological advances as well, demands an ability to adapt to rapid change. Change in our frame of reference, change in the parameters of our everyday world, is continual and is increasing rapidly. Training in specific skills, greater and greater specialization, is a desperate and misguided reaction to such change. It is self-defeating, for today's specialty is replaced by tomorrow's new need.

The main task, then, is to train people who can adapt to change. In choosing the methods of education, it would be well to heed the advice the philosopher Alfred North Whitehead gave more than 25 years ago, for it is even more true today:

> It is of no use to train the young in one very special process which will probably be superseded before they are middle-aged. Give them alert minds exercised in observation and in reasoning, with some knowledge of the world about them, and with feeling for beauty.

Chapter 6

THREE PROMISING AREAS OF SYSTEMS RESEARCH AND THEIR IMPACT ON BUSINESS

Systems research, based upon an interaction among many areas of scientific inquiry, will significantly advance the application of modern information technology to a variety of human tasks. Research into advanced systems design in the business environment, modified by knowledge gained in scientific fields, will result in new and powerful analytical tools for management, and in new concepts of business organization itself. Three potentially significant areas of systems research are described.

This chapter is based on a paper presented before the International Cybernetic Association, Namur, Belgium.

We are on the threshold of what I believe to be yet another quantum step in the development of automation. This development is not based on any single new scientific discovery as much as it is based on an interaction among existing sciences.

Scientists in diverse fields are exploring the basic control systems underlying their respective disciplines. It is becoming more apparent that future technological innovations will not be based alone on single new discoveries but will result to an increasing degree from an interaction among many areas of scientific inquiry. Such interdisciplinary activity will significantly advance the application of modern information machines to a variety of human systems.

An important area of research is *heuristics*—the study of the processes of problem solving. Based on these studies, efforts are being made to build goal-seeking systems by means of electronic computers. Such machine systems will not only make choices between alternative courses of action needed to arrive at predetermined goals; they will also "learn" in much the sense of that word as used in referring to human beings. The impact of such technology will be felt in the business environment in the form of new and powerful analytical tools for management and new concepts of business organization.

The past decade saw the perfection of computers that far exceeded our ability to use them effectively. This has been caused in part by a lack of understanding of the systems to be controlled. In the coming decade, the gap between machine and system should lessen. Present research efforts will yield a greater knowledge about complex systems in several areas: biological, physical, and social.

Research into basic control systems is developing primarily along three lines:

1. Heuristics—research into problem-solving procedures
2. Artificial intelligence systems
3. Simulation of basic neural elements and physiological processes

1. *Heuristics*

Heuristics research seeks to discover and imitate the processes of problem solving employed by human beings. It does this by investigating human behavior at the observable level. Heuristics attempts to determine human problem-solving processes by isolating the *steps* used by people to arrive at solutions to various complex problems. Heuristic computer programs are being devised that will aid in the resolution of specific human decisions. In addition, these programs will provide a general problem-solving procedure that can be used to attack diverse questions. The tool for the simulation is a program written for a general purpose computer.

Two separate but closely related lines of investigation have developed in this research. One approach involves the intensive study of human problem-solving processes leading to the solution of a *particular* problem or goal in order to determine the heuristics—the selectivity in exploration and the development of specific rules of thumb—used by a person in solving the problem. The other approach aims at studying *general* problem-solving methods rather than the methods of solving a particular situation.

As to the particularized approach, programs to solve a special problem have been designed for a variety of specific questions that involve decisions of a qualitative as well as quantitative nature. For example, an investment banker was studied intensively and interviewed to determine how he made stock selections. From the information obtained a computer was programmed to imitate the functions and thought processes of the banker, and the computer in turn designed an investment portfolio. The design of motors drawn to given specifications by a computer can be considered another "heuristic-type" program; one such is used by at least two manufacturers. Similar programs have been written for the design of transformers and other electronic devices. In another simulation of a more experimental nature, the purchase decisions of a department store buyer were studied: based on inventory levels, sales forecasts, and sales prices, decisions were made for markdowns and purchases.

Machines can be made to be "goal-oriented." They can be programmed to a certain goal, and they will keep trying new approaches based on the information they are digesting until they work out the best way to arrive at the goal. They improve their approaches as they go along, and, ultimately, they are able to cope with entirely new conditions that may be unknown to the intelligence that built and programmed their electronic innards. Most of the publicity concerning heuristic machines has been devoted to their game-playing abilities, but much of the research being done here and in the Soviet Union is top secret. Both governments know that the next great scientific breakthrough may come in this area.

These machines have special importance in the space program. When the first unmanned spaceship goes to Mars, for instance, no one can predict all the conditions it will meet. But the spaceship's heuristic system can be given goals of landing, exploring, and returning, and it will accomplish the mission in the best possible way and adapt itself to whatever conditions it encounters.

Programs have been devised that solve geometric and other mathematical problems and that can play games of chess, checkers, and black jack with varying degrees of intelligence—and, remarkably enough, the computers have defeated the men who taught them. To date these programs are still quite limited in their development.

Other heuristic applications are now taken for granted and are only awaiting financing and public acceptance. On the electronic highways of the future the driver may dial a destination and let his computer-controlled car pick the optimum route and do the driving. Teaching machines already in use pace a student's progress, diagnose his weaknesses, and make certain that he understands a fundamental concept before allowing him to advance to the next lesson. Computers will enable a businessman to test all the alternatives of a decision before he actually consummates a transaction. And the State Department will someday, to a limited extent, be able to feed the factors of a ticklish international situation into a computer and learn the probable consequences to each of a wide range of decisions.

The second line of heuristic investigation is aimed at trying to devise a generalized program of human problem-solving rather than one directed at a specific goal. Such general programs are so structured that they can be adapted to the solution of a variety of problems for which basic data are provided.

The best known of these programs is probably the General

Problem Solver Program (GPS) devised by Newell and Simon. GPS provides the analysis mechanism by which diverse types of problems may be solved. This program has been used already to solve trigonometric problems, and it has been adapted to solving certain puzzles. Simon has also shown, theoretically, how the GPS can explain the process of human learning in general and, specifically, in the problem of learning speech.

One company, the Systems Development Corporation, has attempted a general approach to the simulation of the thought processes of a business executive based on non-empirical studies. This simulation uses statistical descriptions of time allocation and availability of the executive (e.g., interactions with subordinates) and other quantitative descriptors in simulating an individual executive.

2. *Artificial Intelligence Systems Research*

This research work seeks to devise machine processes that can solve complex problems regardless of whether the process is human-imitative or not. (While this category can be considered as encompassing the heuristic programming category, as well as neural and physiological simulations, the approach and rate of progress in each category are different.)

Artificial intelligence has been divided into five main areas: search, pattern recognition, learning, planning, and induction. Planning, induction, and to some extent learning come under the category of complex human task simulations, or heuristics, which has been considered previously. Theoretical work in "search" is under way to determine means for reducing the number of possible solutions to any given problem to a small number of meaningfully acceptable solutions.

A practical outgrowth of investigation into search problems may result in more effective information retrieval systems. This can be important in the more rapid retrieval of library information and in industrial research. Another benefit of "search" research should be improvements in language translation systems. This work will materially contribute to "concept" language translation, essentially similar in effectiveness to a human translator, as opposed to mechanical language translation, which is usually based on a word-for-word translation.*

Pattern recognition research has been going on both at the theoretical and experimental levels. General purpose and special purpose computing devices have aided in testing out theoretical knowledge of pattern recognition. The perceptron is a device which can distinguish visible characters, such as letters of the alphabet, identify objects, and recognize faces. It is an analog of the human eye mechanism. Other character-sensing devices employ specific heuristics for visible character recognition. In other words, they simulate the particular rules which humans use to isolate distinguishing properties for character identification. At the present time, these devices are not generally applicable to *all* character sensing. Rather they are limited for practical reasons to preconceived test patterns determined by the human designers for differentiation between small selected groups of characters.

Voice pattern recognition also falls within this category

* Much work is going on in devising a universal symbolic language that can serve an intermediate function in translations from any one language to any other. The method used in such systems is: going from language A to the universal language then to language B, where A and B are the human languages involved.

of pattern recognition research. Special purpose devices can distinguish between limited numbers of voice inputs, but research is still far from perfecting an input device for feeding oral data to a computer system. Substantial progress in sound pattern recognition has been made where the sound to be recognized is simpler than the human voice. For example, direct interpretation of Morse code into English has been accomplished to a degree that is comparable in effectiveness to a human operator. The system is based on statistical analysis of human-sent code signals.

3. Research in Simulation of Basic Neural Elements and Physiological Processes

This work attempts to duplicate the reactions of basic neural elements to stimuli and various physiological control systems. Such research is fundamental to the development of what are called "self-organizing" and "adaptive" control systems. Here again theoretical concepts of human physiological processes can be tested by computer simulation to determine their verity.

The perceptron discussed previously is just such an analog. Designed by a psychologist, the device is based on scientists' concepts of how the eye and nerves distinguish different patterns. Developments in pattern recognition, whether they be in sight or sound, will depend to a great extent on the accurateness of our interpretation of these human processes.

Since the human body itself is such an outstanding example of a control system with extraordinary adaptive powers for different environments, it has served as the focal point for control systems research among those who seek greater understanding of all physical systems. This is perhaps best exemplified by the university which has a biological computer laboratory under the wing of its electrical engineering department, or the research going on in another university's electrical engineering department into the control aspects of the glucose level in the bloodstream. While the number of people working in these areas is not great compared with the total world scientific effort, the research efforts noted here are far from isolated examples.

Applicability of Control Systems Research. Research in each of the three areas delineated above will undoubtedly yield practical applications in the future. Present developments indicate that the first area—simulations into complex human problem-solving processes—will be of great importance within the next few years. This will include increased use of detailed analysis of specific problems, with "heuristics" developed by approximating the human decision-making rules. There are still a great many problems standing in the way of devising a more generalized program that would solve any problem encountered by humans. The empirical data about how humans solve intricate problems are still small—too small to unlock the puzzle of the human brain. However, the data are sizable enough to imitate the observable (or more superficial) aspects of man's behavior.

Herbert A. Simon distinguishes between three levels of explanation for human thinking processes:

> At the highest (but least fundamental) level will be information processing theories of overt behavior. At the next level will be neurological theories explaining how elementary information processes are implemented in the brain. At a still more fundamental level will be biochemical theories reducing the neurological mechanisms to physical and chemical terms. Information processing theories and biochemical theories are complementary, not competitive scientific commodities. We shall need all three

kinds and perhaps others as well before we shall understand the human mind.

He adds, however, "We do assert that, at a grosser level, the computer can be organized to imitate the human brain." Even if progress is limited in this short term to this "grosser level" of human imitation, it still has been demonstrated that the solutions to complex problems in human affairs will involve the computer in the near future.

Research of the kind described here is certainly not an end in itself. Rather it is a point of departure for the understanding of control mechanisms in a variety of disciplines. If scientists are correct in their contention that there is an essential interdisciplinary character in control systems, further understanding of such mechanisms in one science will materially advance knowledge in other areas concerned with control.

Here are a few examples of fundamental questions now under investigation where control systems research offers the promise of solution within this decade:

1. *Biology*

Zoologists are unravelling the organization and development of the embryonic cell. Physiologists are attempting to simulate the behavior of the human metabolic system with its ability to adapt to changing environmental conditions. And neurophysiologists are trying to simulate the basic neural elements involved in the thought process and the nervous system—the neuron (this research may eventually lead to more knowledge about how the brain functions).

2. *Psychology*

Clinicians are studying abnormal human behavior in an effort to devise means of controlling and correcting it.

Theorists are refining their concepts of the human learning process (this research may result in the simulation of sense perception).

3. *Economics*

Econometricians are attempting to construct mathematical models of the economy in order to gain a better understanding of the business cycle. This would enable economists to anticipate fluctuations and minimize their effects. Input-output mathematical models of the economy have been constructed, and are continually in the process of refinement. These will indicate aggregate industrial needs on a national scale.

4. *Control Engineering*

Aeronautical engineers are developing simulations of complex high-speed flight patterns. These will be used for mathematical models of new missile designs and will minimize the necessity for the construction of expensive prototypes before the systems are perfected.

Chemical engineers are working on ways to achieve better control of those processes where they still have a limited knowledge of the kinetic reaction involved. They are also trying to devise systems that will analyze a process under controlled conditions and determine its key operational variables.

5. *National Defense*

Economists, mathematicians, engineers, and others are constructing systems that will outline defense strategies within minutes in the face of any combination of enemy weaponry hurled at us in an attack situation. Time considerations necessitate that the task of devising such a strategy must fall mainly upon machines.

Military strategists are designing systems that will help in evaluating a potential enemy's defense planning. These systems will then furnish instructions for making our defense program a more effective one in the light of calculations on enemy maneuvers.

The Impact on Management

One thing is certain: the business world will be acutely and permanently affected by the impact of this advanced research. In fact, business itself has become the subject of "systems" research. Even now, it is possible to distinguish a recent discipline emerging from the subjective shadows of art into the harsh glare of science—the management sciences. This novice in the scientific community is already considering a series of problems analogous to those under consideration in other scientific disciplines.

The following indicates characteristics found to be common to almost all systems of management:

1. Management systems are highly complex in nature. It is virtually impossible to relate the components (or systems variables) in a quantitative fashion; in certain cases, the critical variables cannot even be identified.

2. In many cases, business systems exist in an unstructured environment; that is, it is difficult to determine where the system to be considered leaves off and where it begins.

3. Any significant approach to the control of these systems demands the processing of large quantities of data at very high speeds. However, these systems, and the problems encountered in their control, often cannot be described with conventional mathematical methods. At the present time, qualitative factors necessary to a systems description in a

business context can only be depicted in terms of a human being.

Almost any policy question facing top management will be characterized by some or all of these complicating factors. Even many problems at lower management levels are too complex to be solved satisfactorily on the computer with presently available techniques.

To date businesses have used computer hardware primarily for the limited function of statistical data processing. When data are processed (or manipulated) in some way, information results that can be used by a human to make a "control" decision. This use of information for control purposes might be called "information processing." When companies begin to utilize more completely the potential of computers through the application of increased knowledge of control systems, i.e., when computers are used for *information* processing in addition to *data* processing, then management can expect some dramatic results. Following are some examples.

Manufacturing. Computers have already been utilized to maintain up-to-the-minute information about inventory levels, production operations, and production costs. Hours worked by employees and wage rate data have been processed effectively to yield payroll information. Control of inventory levels has been achieved in many places by the use of fixed formula techniques, and the routing, scheduling, and follow-up of production processes have been successfully computerized.

However, only recently has an attempt been made to integrate the decisions concerning inventory, production, output, and employment levels into *one* interdependent decision system. In such a system, the behavior of these critical variables has been analyzed as they affect one another, forecasts have been made of future product demands based on statistical analyses of historical data, and optimal schedules for each of the variables have been determined. Fairly successful results have been obtained in factory operations where such a system has been installed.

One system has been made available by a computer manufacturer that provides the framework for the complete automation of a manufacturer's production that also includes its distribution operations. It starts at the point of a sales forecast and incorporates purchasing decisions, order processing, maintenance of inventory levels, control of production operations, product storage, and finally, distribution.

Marketing. Detailed costs analysis on the computer of each salesman's efforts is now possible. This is done by calculating time spent in selling each of the products in the company's line, by measuring the product's contributions to profit, and by determining expenses incurred during the sales effort. Based on this type of cost data, it is possible to devise idealized schedules for salesmen's calls by using linear programming techniques. Optimum distribution points for products can be determined through the same techniques. A quantitative approach has also been taken to determine proper advertising budgets. The approach is based on analysis of advertising costs, percentage of market obtained with past expenditures, market objectives of the company, and other strategic considerations.

More sophisticated application of information processing will enable management to look at the *total* marketing operation as a unified whole. In one case, a company has attempted to devise a model for operational purposes that incorporates the whole marketing environment in which the company does business. In this particular situation the mathematical problem is simplified because (1) there are a small number of products; (2) they are nationally distributed; (3) they are affected by national economic trends; and (4) the firm has few competitors.

Corporate Organization. Several corporations are presently analyzing their total information network. For example, one company is trying to determine the flow of information throughout its entire management hierarchy that is required in the making of decisions. Once this has been done, a mathematical model of the information system will be set up.

Another large multiproduct, multi-industry corporation plans to install a computer communications network for the entire company. This central system will serve as a clearing house for messages that are sent within the company from one location to another. At the same time, the computer system will handle regular data processing tasks for the company.

Finance. A number of banks have installed (or have ordered) similar communications systems that allow each teller to have direct contact with a central memory unit. This unit maintains all customer accounts. It allows the teller at any of the bank's branch locations to update a customer's account as the customer is making a transaction.

With the exception of the limited examples cited above, creative use of information processing in business has not been realized. The great obstacle to this advance lies in the lack of understanding of the processes by which higher management decisions are made. Two significant hurdles must be overcome before it is possible to introduce automated control systems as a supplement to decision structures, such as corporations:

First, it is necessary to understand the basic fabric of human communication patterns in complex organizations. The larger the organization, the more products (or tasks) it is concerned with, the less structured its operating environment (each of these factors increases the difficulty of determining its information system). The empirical task of gathering data in such cases is great. However, it is not insurmountable. The availability of electronic computers makes the job one of manageable proportions.

Second, as yet scientists cannot artificially imitate intelligent human behavior in an unstructured environment. At the present time, from a technical standpoint, machine systems are limited in usefulness to situations in which the decision to be reached can be quantified into an algorithmic relationship, and the quantification thus made will still approximate at least the real world environment sufficiently to be useful.

The first obstacle—the need to learn more about complex communications systems—can be overcome by industrious application. While it would be difficult to say when the second limitation—the limitation of human behavior in an unstructured environment—will be overcome, many scientists believe that it will be surmounted eventually. Such an achievement will depend largely on the ingenuity of the sciences.

Automation and Improved Management Control

Precomputer Control Systems. Prior to the introduction of the computer, management control was achieved in all companies through summary historical reports submitted weeks or months "after the fact." These reports told how well the business had operated at some point in the past. Management then used historical analyses of certain selected indicators of the company's operations as a guide to assist in planning for the future of the business. This is still the way a majority of firms do their long range planning.

The limitations of such a system are obvious. Top management cannot have up-to-date knowledge of present operations by this system except that which it can surmise from outdated reports. Lack of current information reduces the lead time required by management to respond successfully to new competitive situations. Furthermore, such companies generally are forced to operate along strictly functional lines with little awareness or study of the interrelationships that decisions in one functional area have on another.

Real-time Operational Control. The next level of management control makes full utilization of present electronic data processing hardware to monitor *present* operations. From a technical standpoint, multilocational companies should be able to integrate their various locations by means of a high-speed digital communications system. Data can be fed into a central processor from "satellite" computers or from transmission units located in the individual plants. Such data can then be summarized for top management reports. In other words, it is now technically possible to monitor the exact state of affairs in a complex organization during its actual operation.

Ultimately, it should be possible to use real-time (or up-to-date) operational data to modify present operations. In order for the computer to do more than just monitor present operations, it will be necessary to develop a "model" or simulation of the operation to be controlled. The model then receives inputs of operational data and notes deviations from ideal operation according to the value system built into the model. When a deviation from optimal operation is detected by the simulated system, self-correction routines can be initiated automatically.

While the hardware available today makes it feasible to devise systems that can monitor present operations, there still is not sufficient knowledge of the complex workings of a business system to superimpose a working model on an operating corporation so that modifications or corrections can be made. Real-time systems have proven practical in such industries as banking and air transportation because in these industries there are a limited number of variables necessary to describe the operational environment. The difficulties in obtaining similar operation information in a multilocational, multiproduct manufacturing company are significantly greater. A real-time communications network has not yet been established for such a company.

Automatic Controls. Several large manufacturing corporations in the United States are actively attempting to devise corporation information networks that can be used eventually as the basis for a computer controlled centralized data gathering system. However, even if these companies succeed in developing such a complex information network, they will still fall far short of the major task of formulating an operational model of the company from which to achieve the next level of control. This consists of superimposing the model on the information control system in order to achieve some degree of *automatic* control over operations. Such systems are still in the future as far as the business world is concerned.

The greatest progress in devising automatic control systems has been made by the military. SAGE (Semi-Automatic Ground Environment), a continental air command and warning system, is a good example of the advantages and some of the limitations of a centralized, real-time, simulation-based system. Its function is "to maintain a complete, up-to-date picture of the air and ground situation in the continental United States and other parts of North America, to control modern air defense weapons rapidly and accurately, and present appropriated filtered pictures of the air and weapons situation to air force personnel who conduct the air battle." The system employs a vast series of interconnected air defense direction centers. These centers collect and process the data they receive on air movements, displays, information, and other aids in weapons assignments. Since every flight must be monitored and there are more than 50,000 flights daily in the United States, the system operates "by exception." After a flight has been identified by several means, it is not considered any further.

The SAGE-type system has made three significant contributions to the design of management control systems: (1) the SAGE system proved the possibility of an on-line, direct read-in/read-out, integrated computer operation; (2) management by exception was proven for a large-scale data processing operation with masses of data sorted by built-in criteria; and (3) it demonstrated that interrogation, or fast simulation possibilities, could be built into such a system.

While these features are obviously desirable and necessary in a management control system, they still do not solve some of the key problems in adapting a system with this level of control to industrial management. One writer, commenting on the programming task in management control systems, stated: "The computer program must be comprehensive enough to handle a wide variety of possible situations and must include *precise rules* (or formulas) for handling these situations. . . . Once the situation to be controlled is recognized and the rules determined, the task of designing the program can be done."

The difficulties involved in assigning "precise rules," or formulas, seem to preclude immediate progress in devising a top management planning and control system. While the very nature of the top management function is concerned for the most part with planning and control, it demands the inclusion of a number of qualitative considerations that cannot be constrained within the bounds of strict mathematical (or algorithmic) relationships.

The limitations on the number of preconceived plans that can be programmed at any one time puts a strain on the control system's adaptability to changing situations. This is an especially serious problem when the attempt is made to design a system for operation in an industrial as opposed to a military environment. In this modern age of high-speed missiles and jet aircraft, the military environment seems the more complex. Yet it is a considerably simpler environment than the industrial or commercial world. In a military situation the parameters (e.g., the quantities and distribution of attack weapons) of the variables (e.g., the types of weapons used) may be difficult to ascertain. However, in the industrial environment it is still impossible to *identify* correctly all the pertinent variables themselves, much less attempt to circumscribe them.

Military strategy, with all the difficulties implicit in a variety of possible attack situations, is still a relatively structured problem compared with the complexities of the industrial world. The "two-person game" concept, of some practical value in the military world, has little or no applicability in the "*n* person" environment of business.

Another limitation of the SAGE-type system is the key role of the human decision maker in devising basic strategy. In the SAGE system, the basic *allocation* of weapons is decided by a human; the computer plays a major role in further direction of the weapon to the target. Dependence on a human decision maker in our present military environment is hazardous, to say the least. With the constantly decreasing lead time between attack alert and actual strike, with the increasing variety of weapons available, the allocation (or planning, in the industrial environment) role in the system is crucial. Yet at this stage in systems development, the allocation problem cannot be surmounted without considerable human intervention.

Finally, the military environment is an essentially physical system. Once the decision has been made to wage war, strategy considerations will be based on a limited number of objectives with easily definable fields of competition.

This discussion is not meant to minimize the complexity of military defense problems. Rather it is to focus attention on the much greater complexity of the nonmilitary business environment. There is *no* control system comparable to SAGE operating in the industrial environment. It is important to emphasize again: industry is still attempting to design the first corporate *information* system. The ability to superimpose a control capacity on top of that information system is still a long way from realization.

Interestingly, it is possible to anticipate the limitations of corporate control systems, once they are operative, even though they are thus far only in the experimental stage:

1. Such systems will be limited in efficacy by the systems designer's knowledge of the system (or company) to be controlled. Any such designer-created simulation will react repeatedly in a manner determined by the values of the human designer. It will be flexible only to the extent that an alternative situation or course of action was foreseen and anticipated by the systems designer.

2. There will still be a great deal of difficulty in identifying and relating the critical factors necessary to arrive at top managerial decisions.

3. There will remain many qualitative factors that must be considered in formulating company policy that cannot be reduced to mathematical notation. This is especially true in such judgment areas as the evaluation of competitive alternatives, analyzing market strategy, or the design of an advertising policy.

Heuristics and Automatic Controls. It is interesting to speculate a bit about the next improvement in management control: a real-time operation control system incorporating heuristic programming characteristics. Artificial contrivances will become so sophisticated that they will demonstrate a high degree of capability for the solution of unstructured problems. These tools will advance beyond the limitations of a fixed algorithmic simulation of a business problem and will provide a continuous and automatic control that simulates human intelligence and judgment for management control purposes.

It is difficult to find evidence that we are prepared to incorporate these advanced systems effectively once they become available. If history is our guide as to what can be expected of human behavior in the near future, the chances are very good that we will not be ready to utilize or integrate these potent tools into our industrial life when they finally do emerge from their present developmental stages into tangible, workable instruments.

Chapter 7

THE LONG VIEW OF HISTORY—
AND ITS VALUE TO THE BUSINESSMAN

There is a tendency to treat technological developments as awe-deserving achievements, but withal as single, disparate contributions to progress. Rarely do managers have the insight to recognize today's innovations as part of the great continuum of changing society itself. But only from a long-range viewpoint can the true meaning of modern technology be grasped. As the machines of yesterday were significant because they altered the society into which they were introduced, so today's innovations will reshape modern society. Such a view will enable managers not only to put today's new developments in perspective, but also to define the context in which tomorrow's technology will emerge and to understand as well the way the business enterprise must change in response to the changing character of the

111

social environment—which is the ultimate determinant of the role and character of the business enterprise.

This chapter is based on an address given before the annual meeting of the Society for the History of Technology, held in conjunction with the annual meeting of the American Association for the Advancement of Science, New York.

The long view of history confirms that it is in the social changes wrought by the new technology that the real meaning of our current revolution lies. While it is difficult to say precisely what forms these changes will take, it is apparent that they will permeate every aspect of our lives— that they will touch the very philosophical roots of our culture. The artistic, religious, and moral, as well as the political and economic perspectives of men will be affected irreversibly by machines which, as I have already pointed out, must alter the individual's very concept of himself and his relationship to the universe.

No realization could be more important to the businessman. All too often we accept the individual developments of technology as unique inventions, interesting and even significant steps in the evolution of a machine, or process, or discipline—in other words, a product of today's society. Rarely do we view them as part of a great continuum which is bringing about a change in society itself. Yet that is what is happening. And it is my own belief that if there were ever a time when the study of the history of technology was of consequence to the human race, this surely is it. To gain better understanding of the process of technological change and of the human meaning of that change is to gain sorely needed insight into the history of our own times. Since we live in a time when technological change comes upon us with a speed and consequence never before experienced in human history, it is entirely fitting that we search history for such insight.

My friend Robert Heilbroner has called a recent book of his *The Future as History*. This phrase appeals to me for it provides a useful challenge. If we can learn to interpret today's developments, and those we forecast for the coming decade, not as finite inventions or simply new machines, but in the perspective of history, then we are in a vastly improved position to conduct ourselves better in other aspects of our society. This perspective is of enormous importance to today's businessman in setting business policy. Automation is an excellent case in point.

For fifteen years now we have been applying to industry, government, and business the technological developments fundamental to automation. The technology itself, of course, has been in evidence even longer than this. Yet we have had to be dragged, screaming and shouting that there really was nothing new—or at least not both new and "practical"—every step of the way! Each development in turn is first decried as visionary, blue sky, or "cloud 19"; next it becomes "practical"—because someone tries it properly and finds it economically justified; when it becomes generally accepted it is described as nothing new after all.

In the late 1940s credence was given to the forecast of a dozen high speed computers being able to handle all calculations in the United States susceptible to such methods. Today, a decade and a half later, we have over 5,000* electronic computers at work and as many again on order. The estimates of the business planning department of my own firm are that between 15,000 and 20,000 will be in use in the United States alone by 1965.

At the 1955 Machine Tool Show in Chicago, I personally interviewed the principal tool builders and found the vast majority considered numerical control a passing fad, impractical and unsuited to the rigors of the shop, despite the

* Note: December, 1960. By mid-1964 there were 16,000 computers.

operation at the show of a handful of systems. At the next show, held this past September, again in Chicago, eight systems were proudly displayed by nearly every firm that said "never" in 1955. The estimates of my own firm are that by the late sixties one-half of all machine tools sold in this country will be numerically controlled.

My point is that we gain little from this conservative view of innovation—only the avoidance of fads—and lose the ability to lead in our use of technology and to avoid being dragged by our heels, victims of rapid changes in technology which alter our business and social structure at random.

The problem, in automation at least, is maintaining a rational basis in looking ahead. The changes, technological and social, are so great and the problems so numerous that to look ahead properly one must balance the difficulty of bringing about even simple change with the inevitability of great change.

But it is not so pedantic nor so difficult either that we should shy away from it. How then will the facets of this many-sided development of automation stand up in the long view of history? Those that received the most widespread attention at first were:

Machines that performed automatically a long and often complicated sequence of functions from pretzel bending to the assembly of aircraft engines; transfer machines, a natural evolution of both the machine tool and the assembly line—the linking together of machine stations until not only hundreds, but now over one thousand metal cutting functions are performed without human intervention; and integrated systems of automatic machine tool and transfer devices and automatic materials handling equipment.

These often spectacular developments constitute much of the public image of automation, and, in particular industries utilizing long product runs (and recently not so long runs), all are a development of major economic significance. But in many other ways, and certainly in the long view of history, these developments are trivial. They are one further improvement in the state of the art of metalworking and fabrication.

Far more significant are developments in information theory, communications, and control. These have already led to an interesting and significant technology:

With electronic computers, numerical control not only of machine tools but of assembly machines and transfer devices is for the first time possible. This permits flexible automatic systems, adaptable to the varied product and short runs of the conventional production shop, and computer control of process plants—power generation, petrochemical manufacture, steel rolling, atomic facilities, pulp and paper manufacture—where start up and monitoring, as well as automatic optimum operation, are made possible by use of a computer, communication, and control system.

Common to these examples is the application of information technology. While "Detroit automation" may be peripheral, control and information technology is at the heart of the truly significant part of the automation development.

While its roots are far in the past—steering engines of ships, Watt's governor, Dutch windmills, Roman float control, Chinese chariot linkage systems—the technology of feedback applied on any wide scale is a phenomenon of our own times.

All great ideas are simple and never "new" in the sense of being created in a vacuum, or first exemplified; but the self-conscious realization of the possible use and ramifications of an idea is.

• To say of Freud that the Greek playwrights or the Russian novelists educed and used many of his concepts does not derogate from the newness of his insights.

• Or to point to early Christian communal theories, or even to historians who considered economic factors, does not vitiate the force of Marx's economic determinism.

• The theory of interchangeable parts was revolutionary regardless of whether any particular factory previously used it, because after Whitney society became aware of its implications in the production of goods.

So with the feedback principle. Historians do not have to search for particular mechanical devices to show its prior existence, for we are all aware of the interaction of our sense perceptions and brain—true feedback circuitry. What is new is our conscious awareness of the potentials of this idea, and what will be revolutionary will be the effects of the application of this technology on our society.

Thus, in looking at automation as a development in the history of technology, communication and control will be the central core of what we and future generations must recognize to be the truly significant development.

Yet even here we must back off still further, for it is not the technology that will be the historical significance of automation.

If we adopt the long view of history, I am convinced that

it is to the social change brought on by technology that we must look for the real meaning of our current technological revolution. After all, it is to this change that we really apply the word *revolution*, not to the machines.

The current technological revolution promises to have far wider effects than mere technology. Like James Watt and Richard Arkwright, many of our inventors have no intention of reshaping our entire world. Yet that is what they are unwittingly doing.

Two hundred years ago, when it was necessary for most people to put in sixty or seventy hours a week in miserable factories just in order to survive, the question of what to do with nonwork—with leisure—never presented itself. Today, with our forty hours of work a week, we are already facing the two day weekend with something of a self-conscious attitude. When leisure time spills over from the weekend to Monday and Friday, when a man leaves his desk or station after six hours of work still fresh and full of energy, then, for the first time in history, we will really face the problem of what to do with leisure.

This is a revolution, in other words, which will take us *beyond* the civilization of an industrial society, a revolution in which human beings will be largely freed from the bondage of machines. It will raise an entirely new set of problems: business problems, social problems, and economic problems. It will tax our ingenuity to its utmost. And it will bring about its changes—many of them, at least—within our own lifetime.

What are these changes? In the broadest terms, they are:

• A world in which fewer and fewer people work in factories.

• A world in which less human effort will be required for monotonous and tedious work.

• A world in which the work week is greatly shortened.

• A world in which the pace of life slows down, in which leisure becomes the center of life, rather than the fringe.

It is my estimate that change will permeate every aspect of our life. It is very difficult to guess what form these changes will take, but not that they will occur. I would like to discuss briefly some of the important areas as I see them.

Man's metaphysical concepts must change. Thus, Herbert A. Simon states:

> The developing capacity of computers to simulate man . . . will change man's conception of his own identity as a species. . . . I am confident that man will, as he has in the past, find a new way of describing his place in the universe. . . . But it will be a way as different from the present one as was the Copernican from the Ptolemaic.

The science of psychology will change. The startling fact about computers which play checkers is not how well they play, but that they improve. The current work being done on information systems, programming, and computer language has already brought us to the threshold of a breakthrough in learning theory. We can only guess what such a breakthrough would mean in all phases of education.

Our art will change. Art, whether oriental or Renaissance, has depended on the patronage of the privileged and leisured few. When increased leisure becomes a commonplace and the average man has more and more discretionary energy as well as discretionary income, art may assume a very different place in our lives.

It is my guess that the chrome on American cars was not

a Detroit aberration, but a response to popular demand for art, for decoration, for beauty. (Let us assume that its present abatement heralds improved taste, but not the lessening of this demand.) The mushrooming of arts and crafts courses and the do-it-yourself industries may foreshadow a more general need for aesthetic creativity.

New international trade patterns will evolve. The determinants of comparative advantage, the diversity of markets and supplies, and the disparity of economic development, which are changing so rapidly today, in part reflected the specialization concepts of the industrial revolution. As the integrated systems concepts of automation, as well as the integrated communications and systems capabilities of this new technology, begin to pervade the economic scene, these older systems of trade will change. We already see emerging what David Lilienthal calls the "multinational corporation" —not one company doing business in a foreign country, but an integrated international corporation, staffed and owned by different nationals. (My own consulting business has evolved in this form.)

Language barriers will weaken. Mathematics as well as music have always been universal languages—but few have been able to speak them. With the spread of this new technology and the increasing use of mathematical models and techniques in business, government, and research, there will not only be more people conversant with the language of mathematics, but thought, which is always limited by lingual structure, will be redirected in terms of these new techniques. As lingual provincialism lessens, it is impossible to guess what catholicisms will emerge.

Political outlook will change. We have only to glance at the plethora of legislation growing out of the industrial revolution to know that this new industrial revolution will elicit a political response from our society.

The child labor laws, wage, hour, and working condition regulations were evolved to protect the worker from the excesses of his factory environment, but it will remain for automation to free him from the bondage of the machine. Such quasi-political institutions as labor unions were also developed to meet the special needs of the factory worker. But now that our working force has shifted from the factory to the office, and the office functions are themselves changing, these institutions will have to change or new ones evolve to meet the special needs of the new working force. Perhaps the problem of labor will shift from the prevention of exploitation to the insurance of utilization. Full employment, which we have viewed as an economic necessity, will have to be seen in psychological or cultural terms. (A "featherbed" job which may meet the former need cannot fulfill the latter.)

I do not know what deeper political changes will result. I know that Jefferson's concepts of democracy—with its basic tenet of "that government governs best which governs least"—presupposed an agrarian society. Our own evolution of government welfare responsibility followed the industrialization of our society. Now, as the need of production for survival is surpassed, as poverty and hunger cease to be societal problems, our political concerns will shift—including the balance between individual liberty and social responsibility.

The magnitude of change in business organization which will be brought about by this new technology is far greater than most of us today recognize.

New technology provides the means to build information

systems which transcend the compartmentalized structure of business organization based upon functional specialties. Much of the difficulty that has been experienced in putting these new tools to work in recent years results from the fact that to do so effectively clashes with the fundamental organization system of today's business. The main shift in organization necessary to utilize the new techniques and systems capabilities will result from the integrated as opposed to the departmentalized conception of the business enterprise.

We are today using this technology in only the most elementary manner. New techniques, utilizing computer capabilities, are just beginning to appear on the business scene: *operations research*—the building of mathematical models to solve business problems; *simulation*—using the computer to supply "what would happen if" answers to decision alternatives; and *game theory*—to plan strategically in competitive markets. These are but a few.

The main shift in organization necessary to utilize these new techniques and systems capabilities will result from the integrated as opposed to the departmentalized conception of the business enterprise.

As production is increasingly controlled by a business-wide information system, through computer scheduling and actual factory control, the traditional office-plant distinction requires overhaul.

The role of middle management will change as the function of allocation of resources is performed by computers. Some predict the disappearance of middle management as a line function and the growth of a new staffing function— the analysis and continuing reappraisal of the computer models and of the assumptions on which they are based in order to keep the system sensitive and itself receptive to change.

The advances made in communications, among machines as well as people, now allow for direct, cheap, and immediate flow and feedback of information among any geographic points. Management therefore has a capacity never possible before either to centralize or decentralize its decision functions. Whether or not centralization is appropriate will vary with the situation, but the decision need no longer fall automatically to decentralization.

New techniques will be evolved to enable the effective management of scientific, technical, creative, and service personnel (an increasingly important determinant of business success). This shift in the employment structure has occasioned a large group of problems in how to manage personnel.

Our methods of management have not kept pace with this shift. America has entered this era with a legacy of concepts developed to meet the needs of the *unskilled worker*. Few managements yet understand the essence of the task. The rewards for those that do will be greater as change increases.

Thus looking at automation as an historical development not only helps put today's machines in perspective, but makes clear the context in which tomorrow's technology will both evolve and be put to work.

The value of such a perspective to business and to society simply cannot be overstated. Yet to many—even, I think to most—it still appears an academic exercise. So difficult is it to think of a world which differs in any major way from that in which we live at the moment!

Despite the centuries of looking back and the increasing

rate of change that we see—now in decades rather than in centuries or epochs—we still find it virtually impossible to look ahead. But this will change. And it is in the perspective of history that we will learn to educate ourselves for the future in which we will live out our lives.

Part **3**

THE PUBLIC PROBLEM

Chapter 8

THE PUBLIC ISSUES OF AUTOMATION AND TECHNOLOGICAL CHANGE

Political leaders responsible for the development and execution of public policy find themselves in a dilemma about automation. On the one hand, they are acutely conscious of the possibilities of human dislocation. Their concern is intensified by the lack of reliable information on the probable economic and social impact of this technical revolution. On the other hand, they realize their responsibilities as statesmen to keep this country at the forefront of technical advance. In the last analysis, they have no real choice —technological advance is an irreversible process. Their recourse is not to stop the change, but to avoid or ameliorate any harsh effects of such change, and to insure that new technologies are introduced rapidly enough to insure the economy is kept dynamic and ahead.

The Congress of the United States held its first hearings on the subject in 1955. John Diebold was the first witness called to testify at those hearings. In 1960 a specific request was made to those who had testified in 1955 to update their testimony. Mr. Diebold used this opportunity to identify some of the issues as well as to comment upon the change that has been taking place.

This chapter presents excerpts from the statement of John Diebold before the Joint Economic Committee of the Congress of the United States, August, 1960.

Many of the promises and certainly some of the problems of automation have become realities in American life. The uses of automation that we predicted in 1955 have, for the most part, come to pass. During the few years since the hearings in 1955, automation itself has become an industry. The increases in manufacture of automatic equipment for machine and process control in the factory have been complemented by the phenomenal growth of the electronic data processing equipment industry, serving both factory and office. The whole new field of computer technology has passed from its infancy stages to one of high complexity and sophistication.

Both office and factory automation have been instrumental in increasing our productivity and national output. In fact, their importance in the economy has made it necessary to go beyond thinking of them as simply "tools" of production. Automation, and the concepts it embodies, has become a *national* resource—a source of strength to the nation and a stimulus for technological change.

It is questionable whether we have used this resource as effectively as we should or could, although our achievements seem spectacular. The uses to which we put our energies and the results derived can no longer be compared only with our own historical performance. The world has changed too fast for that. We have seen very graphically in the last few years the results of efforts in the technological area. We have watched our chief competitor, the Soviet Union, make remarkable gains both militarily and economically. If we do not make the fullest use of the techniques we have developed, we may be sure that the Soviets will do just that.

Neither technical nor economic causes have prevented us

from making optimal use of automation. Perhaps the most important single fact surrounding automation has been the *fear* it has engendered—fear of its human consequences. Much of this has been irrational; some of it reasonable. The fact remains that we must improve the environment for achieving technological change.

We are in a critical economic war. The government should do all it can to stimulate private enterprise to produce cheaply and efficiently, and increase the reinvestment rate of business. This calls for a positive national policy toward productivity and technological change. At the same time, government, business, and the community must work together to minimize (and hopefully eliminate) the hardships that may appear locally as a result of rapidly changing economic conditions.

The fact is that we still do not know enough about the effects of automation, or indeed technological change in general, to deal with the problem intelligently. This lack of facts stimulates the fear. In the five years that have elapsed since the initial hearings on automation and technological change, no concerted effort has been made on a national basis to overcome our ignorance.

Some Views That Have Changed

Representative Wright Patman (Dem., Texas, chairman, Joint Economic Committee) specifically asked where I felt that events had reinforced my earlier views and where my views had changed in light of current developments.

In 1955, I stated before the subcommittee that I did not feel that "automation required any special legislation." I still think legislation should not be directed specifically at automation; rather, it was necessary for government to recognize the total problem of coping with technological change.

The hearings, which the subcommittee inaugurated in 1955, stressed the potential impact of automation and technological change on the United States. During the intervening years, this "potential" has partially been realized. The introduction of automation technology has resulted in changes within industry and government. It is not difficult to determine the importance that industry places in automation; the growing amount of industrial capital expenditures for automatic equipment speaks for itself. Unions have recognized automation and have made an issue of it at the collective bargaining tables. The Federal government, in its various agencies, is continually installing substantial amounts of electronic data processing equipment to obtain greater efficiencies (and, indeed, recent Congressional committee hearings were devoted to measuring the effects of electronic data processing in government). Individual state governments have held conferences to consider the economic and social consequences of automation for their states—the Governors of Massachusetts and New York have convened such conferences recently. Automation has become a national issue.

In these last few years other issues have become crystallized in the public's eye: our rate of national economic growth, the political and economic competition with the Soviet Union, the growth of the free world as a source of competition and as a market, and the problems of bringing underdeveloped countries into the twentieth century economically, technologically, and socially. All these issues seem to me to be interdependent with the issue of automation and technological change. We cannot sustain high national growth rate, we cannot compete effectively in the world markets, and we cannot adequately aid foreign countries unless we make the fullest use of our productive capabilities. We have not accomplished this in recent years. I believe we shall have continued difficulties in overcoming our domestic and international problems unless we tackle this issue: how to employ automation and technological change most effectively.

To my mind, there is a clear need for a *national policy* aimed at making the most effective use of technological change. It is not a question of dealing with automation alone. Automation is part of a complex pattern of continuing technological sophistication within our economy. In fact, it is most difficult to isolate the effects of the uses of automation techniques from other change. The Bureau of Labor Statistics, for example, correctly recognized this difficulty when it recently announced the sizable productivity increases in 1959 over 1958. The Bureau pointed out that this increase could not be attributed to one factor alone, but to "the combined effect of a number of interrelated influences, such as skills of workers, managerial skill, changes in technology, capital investment per worker, utilization of capacity, layout and flow of material, and labor-management relations."

The problem, it would seem, is much broader than the "control" of automation through special legislation. We cannot "legislate" automation into existence, just as we cannot legislate its disappearance. Automation is a philosophy of technology—a set of concepts. In itself, it only makes available to us the knowledge of how better to satisfy our material and intellectual desires. Automation does not "cause" anything. To attribute any inherent evils to automation or technological change is like aiming at the shadow instead of the object.

For years we have allowed the turn of phrases such as "Automation causes . . ." erroneously to direct our approach to the subject. These phrases are really shortcut ways of saying, "When we *apply* a set of automation techniques, these sets of results occur." Our own actions or inactions actually *cause* the results.

It has been frequently said that "technological change causes unemployment"; but if a person literally believes this, it is like saying "atomic energy causes war." Atomic energy does not cause war and technological change does not cause unemployment. We know, for example, that the economy is going through a period when the unemployment rate for the unskilled, uneducated worker is much higher than the national average. This state is expected to continue for a long time to come. Is automation or technological change keeping the unskilled worker unemployed? Or rather is there the more basic problem of a failure to eliminate substandard education and training?

It is my belief that the prevailing fear of automation and technological change is totally misdirected. If there must be concern over change, it should be directed toward our own actions in coping with change. We have not even devoted sufficient efforts to examining the "change" phenomenon, and this is necessary before we can act properly.

Ironically enough, the nation presently finds itself in a condition in which it is not making the fullest uses of the available labor manpower and productive capacity, and this at a time when there is an international economic necessity to do the opposite. The national productivity and output have increased only rather sluggishly in recent years.* Original views on the rate of speed at which automation would be introduced were that it would "take a long time to effect." The problems of application are even greater than were anticipated at the time of the initial hearings. Much of the difficulty has not been technological as much as it has been the human problems encountered: introducing new concepts within business organizations not readily adaptable to change, consciousness on the part of management and labor of the need to minimize decreasing employment opportunities within the company, and the like. These kinds of problems have not been solved to a sufficient degree to increase substantially the rate at which automation will be introduced into industry.

In connection with the above problem is the one of education and reeducation. This problem seems more impressive to me now than during the original hearings. The question of what are the changing skill requirements of industry still goes unanswered. On a national scale, we still have not given this question sufficient study, though it has already become a problem among large localized groups of unskilled workers.

Greater understanding of the extent of the problem is needed. A recent study by the state of New York dissected the problem of its future manpower needs and showed what the educational requirements would most likely be in the near future. The Bureau of Labor Statistics through its fine case studies has shed further light on this problem. More

---

* And have continued so to date (1964).

research is needed on a national scale to determine our needs in this area.

Because of some of the difficulties that have developed in the introduction of automation, some of the benefits that I anticipated earlier may not come to pass so readily. I do not expect that excessive leisure will be of concern to us in the near future. The problem of increasing our national output would seem to me to take precedence over this. In the same view, I would not expect any drastic reduction in the average work week figures. In some industries, I would expect that my earlier estimate of decreases in the work week to the low thirties may come to pass (some industries have already achieved this level). However, the greater reductions in work week will probably continue to occur in those industries with high work week levels, agriculture and services.

Views That Have Been Reinforced

I began my original testimony by emphasizing the need "to derive some factual information about automation and its impact upon the economy." This need is more urgent than it was before. While I do not feel that automation has been introduced at as high a rate as has been technically possible, its introduction and its impact have far outstripped what little we have learned about it. My original recommendations included "an outline of a factual study of automation." I have submitted a more complete "guide" to such a study, once again, in the following section in this statement. Studies are still vitally necessary. Academic groups and government agencies have effected fine studies in this area, but they have been limited by serious lack of funds to carry this work further. This would seem to be a proper area for supportable research by all levels of government: Federal, state, and local. Private foundations could also do more to support study in this field. A solid, comprehensive body of facts on the economic and social effects of automation is still nonexistent!

Though we are far from making the best uses of automation, I am most encouraged by the greater recognition that it has received as a new set of concepts rather than as an extension of mechanization. I previously referred to automation as "a basic change in production philosophy . . . a means of organizing or controlling production processes to achieve optimum use of all production resources—mechanical, material, and human."

While industry is far from being organized along these lines, more people are beginning to understand the concepts behind it. We learn of more imaginative uses for automation technology every day.

Many of the feasible applications for automatic controls that I talked about in 1955 are already operational facts, especially in the process industries, where optimal control is now fast approaching. "It makes it possible to do things that you could not do before, in addition to doing the things we have been doing more efficiently." This still seems to me to be the greatest contribution automation can make to our economy.

The new levels of achievement and of being able to do present tasks more efficiently have not been limited to large business organizations. Small businesses can make extensive use of automation techniques both in the factory and the office. Manufacturers have given attention to the design of electronic data processing systems specifically for the use of small business. We have also experienced in recent years the widespread application of the service bureau concept. These bureaus have been designed to care for the needs of smaller organizations without their own computers. In the factory, the availability of flexible machine tools with numerical control may serve to increase the competitive power of a smaller business. My initial opinion that numerical controls would be slow in coming seems to have been borne out. Only recently has this technique started to catch hold in industry, but its rate of acceptance will increase rapidly for years to come.

The total automation industry has grown to major proportions within the economy. In the earlier hearings, the growth potential of the automation industry seemed doubtful to some witnesses on account of what was considered the high investment needed to obtain automation equipment. However, versatile systems, special designs, lower cost per operation, and the service bureaus have succeeded in making automation available to practically all sectors of the business community. According to our estimates, there were more than thirty-five hundred computer systems installed by July 1960. When the initial hearings were held, the systems in operation could be numbered in the dozens. Of this July 1960 total, about twenty-eight hundred were small computer systems. At the same time, we estimate that more than forty-five hundred systems are on order. Our long run projections for this industry put annual sales of electronic data processing equipment well into the billion dollar category. Other sectors of the automation equipment industry, machine and process controls, are expected to grow at comparable rates.

As the installation of this equipment is accomplished, we will begin to notice "where automation is introducing changes in our concepts—in our ways of thinking about management. The organizational structure of business [will] start to shift." I stated this opinion in 1955 and still hold it today.* My feelings now are that the restructuring trend will continue in business organizations. "This makes for many changes in the requirements of what people are doing in firms. It again calls attention to education, and to areas where it is necessary to understand precisely what is happening."

The issue of education has taken on major proportions with respect to business needs: greater need for professional college-trained scientists, engineers, and technicians; less need for unskilled workers. New applied sciences have developed in the last few years which have centered about the concepts of automation, and these sciences have synthesized the worlds of mathematics, electronics, and business. As business grows more sophisticated in its applications of automation, the demand for management personnel trained in these sciences will grow. Now is the time when these people should be trained. I feel quite strongly that this task of training management personnel who can make the fullest use of automation concepts and techniques is not being carried out. With all the profusion of data processing courses and surveys of automation attached to business school curriculums, we have few examples of institutions of higher learning in business which fully integrate the concepts of automation into the entire course of study. One of the bottlenecks, then, in making the fullest use of automation may very well be the lack of adequately trained management manpower.

No doubt, the most prominent aspect of automation is

* And today—1964!

how industry's use of this technology affects employment levels. As pointed out earlier, automation is part of the continuing process of technological change. As part of this change, it has contributed to the "dynamic movements from one industry to another" within the civilian labor force. The long term trend of a decreasing percentage of the labor force engaged in manufacturing will most certainly continue. In the last decade, the manufacturing sector has not only shown percentage decreases, but has decreased in terms of absolute number of employees. Following both the recessions of 1954 and 1958, the manufacturing employment highs have failed to reach prerecession levels. The heavy capital equipment expenditures to automate and mechanize facilities further have certainly contributed in some part to this trend.

Most of the manufacturing employment decreases were in the production work force. This was accompanied by higher employment levels for nonproductive workers, those in the managerial and clerical work force. Recent estimates for this latter sector show it to be perennially behind production workers in raising its productivity and in its absolute productivity as well. In the years to come, we may expect productivity in this sector to rise at a faster rate than it has previously; this should result, to a great extent, from the increased (and more skillful) use of automatic data processing equipment.

The major employment opportunities can be expected in the services and nonmanufacturing, nonagricultural industries. We may expect that in some sectors of the latter category—transportation, public utilities, finance, and insurance —further increases in productivity may affect employment opportunities somewhat.

I would like to reemphasize here my earlier comment that if we are to cope adequately with any human problems arising out of the dislocation of industry, minimized employment levels in certain industries, new skills and educational requirements, we must direct attention to the basic reasons why these problems exist. If industries relocate to new areas, there is a basic problem of stimulating economic growth in the vacated area. If employment levels in certain industries recede, facilities and manpower must be made available to help the displaced develop new skills and obtain different employment. Technological change cannot be encouraged, nor can any temporary problems that may develop in its path be solved, by dealing only symptomatically with the change itself.

ECONOMIC AND SOCIAL ASPECTS OF AUTOMATION

I do not believe that we are presently experiencing the full economic and social influence of automation—that is, of fully utilized automation concepts and techniques. The acceptance of automation techniques by industry has been more gradual than it might have been. Technical or economic feasibility did not hold back the introduction of automation; lack of understanding the new technology, fear, improper planning, and other human mistakes are more likely causes. It would not be too great an exaggeration to say that the economic and social environment had a greater limiting impact on automation than the impact of automation on the environment.

An inspection of the aggregate productivity figures would not reveal any abnormally high productive influence in the postwar economy. Even if the recovery year 1959 is included in productivity calculations, total United States private industry still only had an annual rate of increase in output per man-hour of about 3 per cent for the entire postwar period 1947–59. The nonagricultural sector of the economy had an annual average of about 2½ per cent for the same period. More recent average productivity growth is even lower. The annual average increase in productivity from 1953–59 in nonagricultural industries is slightly less than 2.3 per cent.* In terms of impact on the total economy, it would be difficult to discover where any revolutionary element had been introduced. Of course, substantial productivity gains have been made in a number of individual industries as a result of the introduction of mechanization and automation equipment, but, in some cases, human hardships have developed. In others this has not been so. But in the aggregate sense, automation has not so greatly affected the economy that it can be isolated from advances in technology that we continuously experience.

I do not want to appear to minimize the economic effects of automation. The subcommittee will, no doubt, be provided with many statistics documenting the dislocations of workers and job eliminations attributed to technological change. However, we must avoid incorrectly attributing these results to automation. I made the statement earlier that automation is a set of concepts and techniques, a body of knowledge making available to the nation more efficient means for producing goods. This technology does not cause anything; how we use it yields the results. In other words, how the economy is operating has an influence on what the results will be.

---

* A comparable figure for 1960–1963 is 3.2 per cent.

If normal technological change takes place in a rapidly expanding economy, only the benefits of change are usually noticeable: increased productivity, higher wages, new products, etc. When these same changes take place in a slow moving economy, disruption may occur. The basic issue in this case is not to attack the problem of "change." Clearly, the issue here is the slow growth of the economy.

This may seem like an academic point, but I believe that it is very important to realize this when dealing with the difficult problem of integrating technology in our highly complex economy. There have been times in history when technological developments were so potent and their introduction so rapid that normal economic growth could not accommodate the changes without much human suffering. But I would suggest that in our case we may not be suffering from too rapid an introduction of technology as much as we are experiencing a too slow rate of economic growth—the recent average of about 2.5 per cent.

Economic Aspects

Automation has continued to be most strongly utilized in the manufacturing sector of the economy. The transportation, communication, utilities, finance, and insurance industries are also making use of these concepts to a growing degree.

In terms of the effects on total industry employment, automation has probably most affected the manufacturing sector; I say "probably" because whether the use of automation or mechanization has been more responsible for the decreases in employment needs is still a moot question. The Federal government has also made extensive use of automation techniques; the effects on government employment were investigated recently by the Committee on Post Office and Civil Service of the House of Representatives.

The economic effect on individuals in an industrial situation experiencing the introduction of automation has varied greatly from industry to industry. A lot has depended on what kind of automation technique was being employed, whether it was electronic data processing, "Detroit" automation, process control, or machine tool control. Labor-management relations have also played an important role affecting the outcome. The versatility of the work force, age levels, education levels, all influence what will happen after automation has been installed.

We have generally found that the installation of automation equipment does not lead to mass layoffs of company personnel. Through the means of retraining, natural attrition, transfers, and retirements, dislocation of personnel is minimized. In all cases of successful introduction of automation, management planning for the installation was carefully executed.

Layoffs could not be avoided in all cases. In certain instances, employees were not capable of learning new skills that would be required of them. When transfer possibilities were not available, termination of employment eventually proved necessary. Even here, we found several instances where management maintained the employment level of an operation significantly above what was necessary after the automation equipment was installed. Though it is difficult to generalize that this is standard practice, I have heard others in the field relate this same experience.

Within the last year or two, automation seems to have

become a national issue on two counts. First, on the domestic side, it has caused a good deal of fear. To be more precise, I should say that automation has been used to create fear, specifically, fear of unemployment. Secondly, on the international front, we recognize that we need the production efficiencies that automation allows us if we are to compete effectively in the free world markets. We also need increased productivity if we are to maintain our defense position and yet increase our standard of living. These two positions would seem to contradict each other, but they simultaneously exist.

In some of those industries where it is recognized that displacement of labor has and will continue to occur, some action has been taken. The Armour "automation fund," set up in 1959, attempts to study the "automation problem," tries to find opportunities for employment for workers displaced by automation, and inaugurates retraining programs. This company-financed program is paid for by a levy of one cent per hundred weight of meat shipped, up to a maximum of $500,000 in the fund. The Armour fund has been referred to as having set a pattern for other industries. Several other companies are actually setting up study committees in the Armour fashion. Judging by the publicity received by a company when it embarks on such a program, there seem to be relatively few companies attempting this. However, a start has been made.

It is also encouraging that other institutions have begun to take steps to train both those who are already in the working force and those who will one day join it for the new jobs that automation creates. Several universities, for example, are now offering courses in computer programming, and a number of computer manufacturers are training clerical personnel on the job. A technical high school in Buffalo offers a course in which students build a digital computer and then learn to solve problems with it.

At least one union, Local 1 of the International Brotherhood of Electrical Workers, in St. Louis, in cooperation with the Federal Office of Apprentice Training and a local vocational school, has set up what it calls a "postgraduate school" for training in new electrical techniques. Within a short time, 400 members signed up for a three-year course and were attending 38 different classes four nights a week.

It should be noted that in their demands for a higher minimum wage, a guaranteed annual wage, the four-day week, the granting of specific guarantees, and eventually the control of investments in automation, the issues have been most clearly drawn by organized labor. This is natural, since labor leaders see for labor a direct stake in employment movements. A summary of how labor sees the key issues and how it wants them resolved is found on page 146.

Social Aspects

Automation's social consequences are broader than its economic effects. Results in the social sphere also depend on the speed of introduction of automation. Although automation can influence nearly every phase of our life, there is as great a lack of factual information as there is for the economic questions. Even the immediate effects of automation at the work place are hard to ascertain. There are only a few thorough studies of this subject. The few that exist are not sufficient to come to any generalized conclusions.

AUTOMATION: HOW LABOR SEES THE ISSUES AND THE ACTION TO BE TAKEN

MAJOR ISSUES	ACTION TO BE TAKEN
Industrial	*By industry*

MAJOR ISSUES — *Industrial*	ACTION TO BE TAKEN — *By industry*
• Decreasing job opportunities in manufacturing, mining, and transportation industries.	Through collective bargaining establish provisions for:
• Workers are being "dislocated"; they need more job security.	• Shorter work week.
• Change in wage structure and job evaluation systems.	• Stronger seniority rights.
• Labor not sharing in the gains of productivity from automation.	• Severance payments and other supplementary benefits.
• Industry's labor needs are changing fast; workers must be retrained.	• New systems of compensation, eliminating incentive-type wage payment plans.
	• Higher wages.
	• Earlier retirement.
	• Retraining programs.
	• Special funds to cope with automation problems.

MAJOR ISSUES — *National*	ACTION TO BE TAKEN — *By government*
• The slow rate of economic growth: The GNP should be growing at a 5 per cent annual rate as opposed to the recent 2½ per cent growth trend.	• Stimulate economic growth through increased Federal spending, foster "job-creating, job-inducing programs."
• Rate of increase in real earnings per worker is too low, not as high as early postwar growth rate.	• Promote a Federal training and retraining program.
• Increased number of economically distressed communities.	• Government legislation inducing lower work week levels.
• High sustaining unemployment levels, the possibility of automation leading to "wholesale unemployment and a depression."	• Greater aid to economically distressed communities.
	• State governments should increase unemployment benefit.
	• Change Social Security regulations to provide retirement benefits at earlier age.

Individual studies come to different conclusions, depending on the kind of automation that was introduced (factory automation or electronic data processing), where it was introduced, and the conditions under which the change to automation took place. There have been cases reported, for example, where the introduction of automation in a process plant led to higher morale among the workers, a more highly developed social unit in the plant, and an upgrading in skills. But these reactions have not been true in all cases studied, or even in a majority of the ones that I have seen. A study of an automated assembly line operation reported "increased feelings of tension" among the workers, and this is not an isolated case. Recent studies of automatic data processing installations report a high level of routine work, as high or higher than before the introduction of the automatic equipment. In other establishments, routine work decreased in a comparable situation.

From my own experience, I find that one generalization holds true for the entrance of electronic data processing into an operating unit: there is an increase in the percentage of skilled personnel for the given operation unit after EDP is installed. At the very least, we can see that the newer skills are needed—programmers, systems analysts, systems engineers.

Certain valid generalizations can be made about the needs for retraining programs and, especially, for education. On all levels of working and living we will need more education. Beyond retraining those who already have jobs to prepare them for more highly skilled work, we must face the larger problem of how we are to increase our resources of engineers, scientists, and trained technicians. At present, a good part of our most talented raw material goes to waste every year. About half of the high school students in the upper 25 per cent of their classes do not attend college at all, and another 13 per cent drop out before they finish. All told, almost two thirds of those best fitted to exercise scientific and technical leadership are not being trained to their highest capacity.

This problem will grow more acute in the years ahead, and not only because the need for trained men will grow. We are still drawing heavily on the knowledge and the trained personnel developed under the pressure of military needs. But we cannot go on living off our hump indefinitely. We will have to develop ways of making higher training available to those best suited to make good use of it.

On the high school level, where technicians are trained and where the decision for or against science as a career is often made, the situation is equally acute. High school programs must be reassessed and so must the supply and quality of high school teachers.

But the question of education goes far beyond better training for work in specialized fields. Many of the new jobs that automation will create (supervising the intricate workings of delicate machines, for instance) will require an increasing ability to think and to judge, increased understanding of mathematical and logical methods, in short, increased education in the largest sense of the term. Management will need these abilities on a higher level. And all of us, if our increased leisure is to mean something more than just another day we can sleep late, will need to develop some of these qualities. In view of these needs, one of the great mistakes we could make would be to concentrate all our attention on the specialized problems of educating scientists and technicians.

More than that, the fact that the new machines are capable of providing us with more information than we have ever had raises questions of the highest importance. Just as they can provide answers to scientific questions that could never be answered before, so machines can provide answers to questions outside the field of science that could never be answered before because no one person or group of persons could comprehend all the facts. Man could become a cog in the machine, accepting, in Norbert Wiener's words, "the superior dexterity of the machine-made decisions without too much inquiry as to the motives and principles behind them." It is here that our ability to think, to judge, and to understand will stand us in best stead. For machines are only machines. It is up to men to decide how to use them.

Foreign Aspects of Automation

In the practical application of automation concepts and techniques to industry, the United States leads the world at the present time. In terms of growth rate in application and absolute number of automated installations we are ahead of any country in the free world. I have not included the Communist-bloc nations because there are no substantial data to estimate their progress accurately.

Qualitatively, we know that they are moving ahead at a fast rate. To the extent that they are employing automation, it is interesting to consider Premier Khrushchev's report to the 21st Congress of the Communist Party of the Soviet Union. He gave some indication of the widespread applications intended for mechanization and automation under the Soviet Seven-Year Plan for Economic Development (1959–1965).

Mr. Khrushchev reported that "integrated mechanization and the *automation* of production processes constitute the chief and decisive means for ensuring further technical progress in the economy and, on this basis, a new rise in labour productivity, the lowering of cost prices, and the improvement of the quality of products." This theme is further amplified in Mr. Khrushchev's statement of the "target figures" with regard to level of *automation* to be obtained. Of particular note was the indication of plans for the "establishment of more than 50 experimental model enterprises where the latest patterns of integrated automation will be put into effect."

In a final section, in a discussion of specific provisions of the "plan" as it pertains to educational development, it was stated that "the greatest increase in the number of engineers graduated [during the years of the "plan"] will be in the specialties of chemical technology, *automation*, computing engineering, radio electronics, and other branches of new technique." Stress will also be placed upon scientific development and "in particular [on] the successes of computing mathematics [which] are directly connected with the development of *automation*."

It would be sheer folly to take these words lightly, in view of the Soviet Union's accomplishments in the field of engineering education and in the science of mathematics. Recent reports point to a gap between "theory" and "application" in the field of automation in the Soviet Union. One could not expect this state to last very long (if indeed it is an accurate picture of present achievement levels).

It would also be a mistake to take a complacent attitude toward European business. Though we "out-automate" Europe by sheer volume alone, their level of sophistication in automatic techniques is high, especially in factory automation.

Our company continually surveys the Western European

electronic data processing market. We have found the European attitude to be more cautious to EDP hardware than is true in the United States. The cost factor of automatic equipment is given heavier emphasis. However, we have found that the average European computer user can be expected to make better use of the hardware's capabilities than his American counterpart once it is installed. He has been predisposed by his educational background to accept more easily the theoretical capabilities of the electronic hardware.

Western Europe has a total of over 3,000 computer installations, or about 20 per cent of total United States installations. However, over 90 per cent of this total are small computer system installations. Orders for computer systems number in the thousands for all Western Europe.

Between the Russians on one hand and Western Europe on the other, we really have our hands full. It seems to me that we are in a most tragic plight as a nation when we must worry about the ill-effects of introducing automation—even at a slow rate!

Conclusions

The United States government should formulate a national policy that will effectively stimulate automation and other technological change.

I find it totally unreasonable—and dangerous—that as a nation we permit the waste of a potent national resource, automation. We are faced with a continuous economic and political challenge on the international front that demands sizable outlays for military security, aid to foreign nations, and other international programs. At the same time, we must continually try to raise our material standard of living.

To keep increasing our standard of living and, simultaneously, maintain our economic and political position in the world, we must sustain a high economic growth rate. Real increases in our national output will continue to be heavily influenced by our productivity increases, and productivity increase is a basic result of technological change.

I think we must face up to the fact that we have not made any concerted effort to deal with the problems that retard economic growth. The nation cannot long sustain a high rate of technological advance without coping with these problems; and we simply cannot wait for evolutionary forces to solve our internal problems.

The national policy that will foster automation and technological change should be aimed mainly at bettering the environment for change. (For purposes of formulating national policy, automation should be considered as part of general technological change. It is difficult to separate automation out of the mainstream of change and somewhat useless to do so.) This policy should be geared to set in motion two programs simultaneously.

A program for identifying the effects of automation and technological change within our society should be initiated. We must learn how to stimulate automation to the best advantage and, at the same time, minimize any harmful effects that may accompany it.

Secondly, mechanisms that can encourage economic and technical growth where such growth has stagnated must be designed. I do not feel that this can be accomplished through the efforts of private enterprise acting alone; the resources of local communities and of the state governments are sometimes not sufficient to overcome stagnancy. Individual action by the Federal government is also insufficient.

A cooperative effort employing the resources of all these sectors of the economy must be brought to bear on these problems if they are to be solved. The government can do much to encourage business through an enlightened tax policy and technical aid; communities and states can do more to provide worker training and retraining facilities and assisting in area redevelopment; business can initiate programs to assist employees in adapting to change situations.

A program of continuing study will provide more knowledge on how best to cope with change. It will supply the data needed to influence the social and economic results of the introduction of automation and other technology. However, no study will be of value if it is an expedient to avoid taking action on national issues. The extensive knowledge gathered can, perhaps, be best employed in helping to recognize—in advance—where action should be taken to stimulate technological and economic growth.

It is also very important that through national policy we encourage the widespread application of basic science to industry. Most of the significant innovations of the postwar period have come about through military research programs. Private industry has been unable to make the fullest use of these advances. The government can do much to encourage the dissemination of this kind of information to business. Private enterprise can be further stimulated to employ new techniques and equipment through fiscal policy.

The encouragement of innovation in industry must be supported by labor if we are to achieve its full benefits.

Featherbedding in industry has become a valid issue; it is wasteful not only to the individual company in which it occurs but also to the entire economy. In many instances, labor has shown that it can facilitate change by sponsoring its own retraining programs and by intelligent collective bargaining. The responsibilities of labor in this area will be much greater in the years to come. It remains to be seen whether present labor-management relations, which mainly revolve about periodic collective bargaining sessions, are sufficient to cope with future problems.

These recommendations are far from new. It is vital, however, that they be carried out. I recommended the study of automation at the first congressional hearing on the subject, as others have since. Concerted action of government, community, and business to make the fullest use of this most important national resource—automation—had been suggested previously, although in vain.

It is worth remembering that a national resource, as well as a natural resource, can be lost forever if it is not conserved with intelligence and farsighted planning.

Chapter 9

AT THE STATE LEVEL

Positive programs developed at the state level, particularly with regard to retraining workers and state-sponsored regional development plans, are a large part of the answer to the public problems raised by automation. In the following chapter, a specific program of action for New York State is offered as a guide to public authorities at the state level.

This chapter is based on a working paper prepared for the Governor's Conference on Automation, Cooperstown, New York, June 1–3, 1960.

Automation can be viewed in two ways from the standpoint of New York State:

1. *New York is an important producer of the machines that make up this technological revolution.*

For example, over half the nation's output of electronic computers, and much of the other equipment of automation, are manufactured in New York State. This is a fact which has been given little recognition. Yet it is surely one of the more significant economic consequences of technological change in this state.

2. *The state and its industries are important users of this new equipment.*

Private businesses within the state and the state government itself are important users of new automated equipment and methods. The most significant economic fact regarding new technical developments is that they are an important means of increasing productivity, not by forcing workers to work harder, but by providing a means of reorganizing work and by fruitfully applying scientific and technological innovation. Beyond this, the economic consequences are complex indeed.

New York as a Producer of Automation Equipment

New York is a leader in the production of electronics and control equipment. These are the most rapidly growing areas of new technology and also represent the greatest potential for future growth.

An examination of the electronic computer segment of the industry shows that the two leading producers have the bulk of their facilities located in New York State. International Business Machines, which accounts for over 70 per cent of the nation's total computer production, has over two-thirds of its employment, its four main plants, and most of its research laboratories in the state. The Sperry Rand Corporation, which produces 20 per cent of all computers, as well as other electronic control equipment and instrumentation, likewise has half of its total employment and the main portion of its production and research sites located within the state.

However, this is a fast expanding field. The industry saw a large influx of new controls producers in the years 1950–1960. To sustain the economic advantages it now enjoys as a producer of controls equipment, New York must take positive steps to attract these manufacturers, and, at the same time, keep the "Big Two" in the state.

Furthermore, automation and related industries are in the forefront among all those in the state in terms of recent employment growth. In addition, in each of these industries, the percentage increase in New York State has been greater than for the United States as a whole. These figures forcefully indicate the importance of continuing to stimulate this kind of industry to foster the economic growth of New York State.

Computers are only one segment of this new technology that will have economic impact on New York State. Other facets such as process control, numerical control, and other kinds of automatic data processing equipment will experience extremely rapid growth. In process control manufacture, more than a *three-fold* expansion is forecast; in the numerical controls area, the anticipated growth will be even greater since the absolute base is even smaller.

The presence and continued development of these industries in New York State are a substantial economic asset. This becomes even more noteworthy when it is realized that the level of skills required to produce and service this equipment is very high. The accompanying higher salaries and wages mean increased prosperity for the state. It may be that the historic effort to increase investment in plant and equipment no longer should be a primary consideration in measuring the economic benefit of an industry to the state. The personal income generated by the industry is becoming a better criterion.

How New York Can Encourage Industries Based on New Technology

If New York State is to continue as a leader in these industries, as well as a center for users of the equipment, a positive program must be adopted. Many of the excellent things the state is already doing to attract industry in general should be bolstered. For example, the Community Industrial Resource "Inventories" developed by the Bureau of Industrial Development in cooperation with local chambers of commerce are useful tools. Efforts of this kind must be strengthened by the New York Department of Commerce.

A better business climate should be fostered by stimulating an atmosphere of community progressiveness, eliminating restrictive ordinances and regulations, and making adequate community facilities available. Otherwise, there will be frequent repetitions of a situation already found in one of New York's largest manufacturing companies. This firm, with a bulk of its employment and investment located in New York State, today actually ranks the state near the bottom in its evaluation of new plant locations. As a matter of fact, the firm implies that it would move existing facilities from New York if it were practical or possible.

One of the most important steps that can be taken by the state to attract these new industries is to create a favorable climate for technical personnel. Plant location is increasingly dependent upon the availability of engineers and engineering talent. This is a totally different situation from the unavoidable shifting of the textile industry to the South. The move from Utica and the displacement of 4,000 workers in the early 1950s was caused by a desire to take advantage of lower labor costs and by the technological obsolescence of Utica plants.

In cases where investment in capital equipment is low per employee, and research and development are a key factor, a climate favorable to engineers will attract industry despite the presence of certain other unfavorable considerations. This has a definite multiplier effect in stimulating other industry. The presence of a heavy concentration of engineers together with their high salaries and standards of living will attract other companies. This, of course, is not intended to minimize the importance of other labor costs and availability of labor as a factor in making plant location decisions.

Accordingly, New York should take accelerated steps similar to the recommendations recently established and well conceived by the Advisory Council for the Advancement of Industrial Research and Development. In discussing this report, Governor Rockefeller aptly stated:

> As the nation's leading manufacturing center, New York State has the basic incentive to push forward ceaselessly in the field of industrial research and development. Here are our most

promising growth opportunities for a prosperous economy, long-range industrial expansion and the creation of thousands of new jobs.

The Advisory Council Chairman has recommended that it should work to develop a wider exchange of research institutions: (1) expand the public information program; (2) encourage new research concepts and industrial applications; and (3) develop new educational techniques and legislation. However, this is not enough. The economy of the West Coast moved ahead rapidly in large part because the state had become a research and engineering center. The Rand Corporation in Santa Monica, California, and the research facilities at Stanford University are examples of this development. Accordingly, it is recommended that the following be undertaken in New York:

1. *New York should sponsor the establishment of a technical and research center devoted to information and control technology.* This would bring topmost leaders in engineering and science to the state and would do much to attract other industry. The very presence of top men from whom ideas emanate can do much to draw engineering talent to the state and to develop the state as a research center.

2. *New York should emphasize its many existing strengths in the engineering field.* The state should use its own favorable cultural environment as an attraction to engineers. Many electronics firms have been established on Route 128 near Boston because of the cultural opportunities nearby. These are deemed important by citizens at the high economic levels that generally comprise the engineering talents of these Boston firms.

As an example of existing strength, New York already

has a share of membership in certain key professional associations well ahead of or at least in line with its share of the population. In 1950, memberships of New York State residents in three representative groups were:

	Total U.S.	N.Y. State
Institute of Radio Engineers	73,000	12,000
Association of Computing Machinery ...	5,700	1,000
Instrument Society of America	11,000	1,000

This type of strength needs further emphasis.

3. *New York should strengthen its own efforts in engineering education.* In 1956–57, higher educational institutions in New York State conferred 10 per cent of the national total of first professional degrees in engineering, just in line with the state's share of population. This was due in main part to the efforts of private institutions such as Rensselaer Polytechnic Institute and Columbia University. It is to be noted, however, that of the more than 25 colleges that comprise the State University, only *one* besides the Marine College confers a bachelor's degree in engineering.

Good progress is being made in this direction as indicated by the Governor's appointment of a committee at the end of 1959 to recommend steps for the state to assure college study opportunities, to provide professional training and research facilities, and to contribute its proper share of trained personnel. Particular emphasis should be made for training in the electronic and control fields, as well as provision made for extension courses for older persons.

4. *Training of technicians must be reemphasized and accelerated as an alternative source of skilled manpower.* The increased availability and utilization of persons inter-

mediate in skill between a craftsman and an engineer would do much to attract industry. Often, owing to a dearth of these "quasi-engineers," high priced engineering talent must be employed where these juniors would do as well.

The Need for a Positive Policy for New York State

Of all the 50 states, New York has the largest population, the largest work force, generates the largest share of personal income, and has the largest single part of our gross national product. New York State accounts for 12 per cent of the nation's total personal income and almost 10 per cent of both the total population and labor force. It is only natural that this state should assume aggressive leadership in setting up and fulfilling a positive program for encouraging the widest applications and most creative use of the machines of this new industrial revolution.

The need for a positive program by the state comes into focus forcefully when the recent economic growth of the state is compared to that of the United States as a whole, and to other leading industrial states. Governor Rockefeller has emphasized again and again* that

> The facts demonstrate that our state has been failing to keep pace with the economic growth trend of the rest of the nation. Further, it is lagging behind the income growth rate of most of our neighboring states. Business and industry representing thousands of jobs have left for other states.
>
> It is our responsibility to map policies aimed at creating a favorable climate for job opportunities, reversing the trend of economic exodus, encouraging the expansion of existing business and attracting new business and industry.

* This was in 1958, 1959, and early 1960.

He further cited as the first and final elements of a favorable climate for expansion:

> Recognition of the fundamental identity of the interests of business and labor in economic growth.
>
> Active support by all the agencies of government of policies calculated to create the best possible climate for job opportunities and economic growth.

Within this framework, a positive program designed to develop and implement new technical developments would be a big step in the direction of stimulating the economic growth of the state, as well as the whole nation. Automation is rapidly becoming the accepted norm of business method. Private companies must use it to the fullest in order to survive, just as they must use the best techniques and most efficient methods available in other areas of their businesses. So, too, governments must apply automation and new technology if they are properly to serve the interest of their citizens.

A PROGRAM FOR ACTION

1. *The State of New York should conduct and sponsor detailed studies of the human and economic consequences of automation within the state.*

The importance of gathering data and studying them cannot be overlooked. We do not yet understand the phenomenon we are trying to correct. Automation has become something that everybody wants "to do something about." Some advocates of action sincerely feel that what they propose will mitigate the so-called harmful effects of automation. Some use the fears that automation can arouse to achieve their own goals. Some oppose any investigation because they are sure that everything will work out for the best. There are many theories, many words, and many fears. Above all, there are many proposals about what should be done about automation and other radical new technology.

These suggestions are usually made by a particular group to further its own restricted interests. This is a very dangerous situation for the nation and the state. It is dangerous because there are so few facts about automation and because there is not yet any very systematic way of thinking about its economic and social consequences.

2. *New York should encourage and aid private efforts to adjust to the changes inherent in automating.*

New York can do much to eliminate concern by demonstrating that much of the potential disruption that could be caused by new technology can be solved in a day-to-day manner as each situation arises. Here are several current examples of what has been done in a constructive way to cope with such problems:

a. To take advantage of new jobs becoming available, workers in automated plants need skills that differ from the content of their usual crafts. These include a knowledge of mathematics, physics, electronics, and hydraulics. Special schools have been established by the International Brotherhood of Electrical Workers, and advanced training courses have been organized by the Plumbers and Pipe Fitters Union to fill such needs.

b. The introduction of automatic data processing machines in offices has raised problems of finding personnel for programming, operation, and maintenance.

Generally speaking, larger companies have met these needs through retraining employees selected for their special aptitudes. Other firms with smaller clerical staffs have brought in technicians trained at schools conducted by the equipment manufacturers for such key jobs as programmer, supervisor, and maintenance specialist.

c. In December, 1959, Haloid Xerox, Inc., placed twelve of its employees at the Rochester Institute of Technology for a six-week training course in new skills. Tuition costs as well as wages were paid by the company while the employees were at school. After completing the course, the workers returned to the company.

d. If workers affected cannot be absorbed by their existing employers and cannot get placed in their line of work elsewhere, the community itself may be able to devise means to get them retrained for other jobs. The Utica experience indicates that among workers who become unemployed because of major industrial dislocation, there are many who, with relatively short training periods, could be upgraded to higher levels and different kinds of skills, and that community effort could facilitate this process.

3. Based upon the findings of a detailed study of the new technology and its impact and upon an exploration of the limits of private action, New York must adopt those measures which will insure that no human harm will ensue as a result of pursuing a positive program for utilizing new machines.

Public adoption of such measures will do much to alleviate fear and to lay the basis for a positive program encouraging automation.

While wide-scale legislation may prove unnecessary, there are ways in which existing programs and agencies can be made more helpful in connection with automation. The Section 599 of the State Unemployment Insurance Law is a good example of the kind of legislation the state may wish to adopt. Section 599 provides that a vocational training course may be approved for an unemployment insurance claimant without jeopardizing his benefits. This is an example of a constructive step that will help to make possible the rehabilitation of displaced workers. It is an extension of assistance by the state in an area that can do much to help the worker help himself.

4. *New York should study future educational and training requirements and adopt a comprehensive program that will meet both long and short term needs.*

While it is undoubtedly true that technological changes will cause economic and social upheaval, the most fundamental problem to be faced lies in the area of education and training. Adjustment to change requires a continual process of training. Technical training is one requirement. However, there are other, less obvious, demands.

Business education will be forced to change vastly in the next decade. Not only does the business administrator have new tools, such as the computer, with which he must learn to work, and a changed organizational environment within which to operate as a result of technological developments, he is also faced with a considerable change in his role as administrator. Insufficient attention is being given to this problem today. While it is fashionable to add courses in

PROJECTION OF AVAILABILITY OF NEW DEVELOPMENTS FOR GENERAL SYSTEMS USE

DEVELOPMENT	63	64	65	66	67		69	70	71	72
INFORMATION STORAGE & RETRIEVAL										
HIGH PRICE, LARGE CAPACITY CHIP OR DISCRETE FILM UNIT RECORD SYSTEM OPTICALLY SCANNED			▬▬▬▬▬▬							
HIGH PRICE, LARGE CAPACITY CHIP OR DISCRETE FILM UNIT RECORD SYSTEM MAGNETICALLY SCANNED	▬▬▬▬▬▬▬▬▬▬									
MEDIUM PRICE, LARGE CAPACITY CHIP OR DISCRETE FILM UNIT RECORD SYSTEM— MAGNETICALLY SCANNED			▬▬▬▬▬▬▬▬							
LOW-COST, APERTURE CARD SYSTEM	▬▬▬									
LOW-COST, CHIP OR DISCRETE FILM UNIT RECORD SYSTEM—REPLACE APERTURE CARD SYSTEM						▬▬▬▬▬▬▬▬▬▬				
HIGH PRICE, LARGE CAPACITY, STRIP FILM SYSTEM COMPUTER DRIVEN					▬▬▬▬▬					
MEDIUM PRICE, LARGE CAPACITY, SHEET OR STRIP FILM SYSTEM						▬▬▬▬▬▬▬				
LOW-COST, MEDIUM CAPACITY, SHEET OR STRIP FILM SYSTEM								▬▬▬▬▬▬		
HIGH PRICE, LARGE CAPACITY, CONTINUOUS ROLLED FILM SYSTEM—MAGNETICALLY SCANNED, COMPUTER SEARCH LOGIC							▬▬▬▬▬▬▬			
MEDIUM PRICE, LARGE CAPACITY, CONTINUOUS ROLLED FILM SYSTEM—OPTICALLY SCANNED	▬▬▬▬▬▬▬									
MEDIUM PRICE, LARGE CAPACITY, CONTINUOUS ROLLED FILM SYSTEM MAGNETICALLY SCANNED						▬▬▬				
LOW-COST, MEDIUM CAPACITY, CONTINUOUS ROLLED FILM SYSTEM—OPTICALLY SCANNED					▬▬▬▬▬					
LOW COST, MEDIUM CAPACITY, CONTINUOUS ROLLED FILM SYSTEM—MAGNETICALLY SCANNED						▬▬▬▬▬▬				
HIGH COST, LARGE CAPACITY, CONTINUOUS ROLLED 'ERASABLE' FILM SYSTEM— MAGNETICALLY SCANNED								▬▬▬▬▬▬▬		
MEDIUM COST, MEDIUM CAPACITY, CONTINUOUS ROLLED 'ERASABLE' FILM SYSTEM— MAGNETICALLY SCANNED								▬▬▬▬▬		
DIGITAL FILE STORAGE										
HIGH SPEED MAGNETIC TAPES			▬▬▬▬▬▬▬							
MEDIUM PRICE, HIGH SPEED, READ ONLY, HIGH DENSITY, PHOTO DISK			▬▬▬▬							
MEDIUM PRICE, HIGH DENSITY, PHOTO CHROMATIC MICRO IMAGE STORE							▬▬▬▬▬▬▬▬			
VERY LOW COST, EXPENDABLE DISK STORES						▬▬▬▬▬▬▬▬				
LOW COST, REUSABLE THERMOPLASTIC FILM STORAGE						▬▬▬▬▬▬▬▬				
MEDIUM PRICE, LARGE CAPACITY, PERIPHERAL ASSOCIATIVE DEVICE							▬▬▬▬▬▬			

DIEBOLD GROUP ESTIMATES

PROJECTION OF AVAILABILITY OF NEW DEVELOPMENTS FOR GENERAL SYSTEMS USE

DEVELOPMENT	63	64	65	66	67	68	69	70	71	72
DISPLAYS										
HIGH PRICE, HIGH CAPACITY, LARGE SCREEN OR PANEL PROJECTION DISPLAYS										
MEDIUM PRICE, MEDIUM CAPACITY, CONSOLE DISPLAYS										
HARD COPY OPTIONAL OUTPUT										
COMBINED CHARACTER GENERATING—VIDEO IMAGE INPUT CONSOLE DISPLAY										
LOW COST, INQUIRY CONSOLES										
PRINTER/PLOTTER, NON-IMPACT										
HIGH PRICE, HIGH SPEED MICROFILM RECORDERS										
MEDIUM PRICE, REALTIME, ALPHANUMERIC READOUT PANEL SYSTEMS										
COMMUNICATIONS										
HIGH SPEED DATA INTERCHANGE WITH CODE OR MESSAGE CONVERSION SERVICE										
MEDIUM PRICE, DIGITAL FACSIMILE, FULL PERIOD										
PORTABLE PERSONAL VOICE SERVICE										
LOW COST, DIAL-UP FACSIMILE										
MEDIUM PRICE, DIAL-UP BROAD BAND (UNDER 200KC)										
LASER DATA TRANSMISSION										
HIGH PRICE, DIAL-UP VIDEO-PHONE										
OPTICAL CHARACTER READING										
HIGH PRICE LIMITED FONT PAGE READER (FLYING SPOT SCANNER)										
MEDIUM COST LIMITED FONT PAGE READER (RETINAL)										
HIGHER SPEED MULTIPLE FONT PAGE READER										
LOW COST HIGH CAPACITY MULTIPLE FONT PAGE READER										
LIMITED CHAR. SET HANDWRITTEN DOC. READER										
FULL ALPHANUMERIC HANDWRITTEN DOC. READER										
LOW COST HANDWRITTEN DOC. READER-LIMITED										
LOW COST FULL CHAR. SET HANDWRITTEN DOC. READER										
FIXED FORMAT SINGLE FONT DOCUMENT READER										
LOW COST HIGH SPEED SINGLE FONT FIXED FORMAT DOCUMENT READER										

1st generation
2nd generation

DIEBOLD GROUP ESTIMATES

computers to a program of business training, little if anything is being done to train men for a fundamental change in approach to business.

Another educational ramification that will be encountered is the need for a long-term adjustment to a society in which leisure forms the basis of our culture rather than the fringe. No emphasis is more important here than education. The public consequences of people who badly use what leisure they already have are manifested in headlines on juvenile delinquency, in crime rates, and in a host of other ways, all claiming major corrective attention from government.

This is a long-term problem. Therefore, we have the time for proper planning and adjustment. However, this is not a reason for postponement. New York could do much in setting an example among the states by recognizing this problem and giving to it the major attention it deserves.

5. *New York should actively encourage the industry and commerce of the state to adopt and use automated and other new equipment, with the state government itself leading the way.*

The state can react to this new era in several ways. That it has formally recognized the problems at all, and chosen to study them, stands as a compliment to the state and its leadership. It is a farsighted move. Ensuing legislation and change will be extremely important and will be closely studied by other governmental groups.

If individual businesses within the state are to grow and flourish, or even to continue in existence, there must be an environment conducive to adopting new technology. Maintaining a competitive position requires it; investment by industry within the state will not be attracted without it. It is not a question whether businesses should do this—*they must and they will.*

Therefore, if the economic objectives of New York, as well as the nation, are to be achieved, automation and every development stemming from it must be pursued to the fullest extent possible, and assistance and encouragement from the state government must be provided for increasing productivity by private enterprise.

The state itself should expand more aggressively its own automation program and should serve as a testing ground for other new developments to show what can be done. Installations like the one in the State Tax Department in the Schenectady area are to be applauded and should serve as a model for other departments, other locations, and for private industry.

Several of the state's smaller agencies could establish a jointly operated computer center to demonstrate the operating economies involved and to show smaller businesses and organizational units how they can effectively use such equipment. Computer service bureaus should be encouraged and used by the state. This could illustrate a way small businesses could use automation in their office work. Such action should help to reduce fear by demonstrating the state's own active participation and simultaneously, it would show the applicability of automated methods to small as well as large businesses.

A Positive Atmosphere

The very existence of a positive New York State program fostering automation and other new technology should do much to stimulate other states to follow New York's example, to the benefit of the entire nation. Such a change in atmosphere can insure a more aggressive and imaginative pursuit of the possibilities technology is opening up.

In essence, it is this approach—a positive approach—that is most important. Although the means to bridge the gap between jobs and to prepare persons for new jobs are important, the real need is for sound growth in our economy. The state administration can create such an environment for healthy and vigorous expansion for both the producers and users of automation within the state. To this end, it might be helpful if a resolution such as the following were approved by the New York State legislature:

> SINCE automation and its related fields of technology are both desirable and essential for New York State, and for our nation, in order to achieve our goals of economic growth and continued prosperity, and

> SINCE New York State is aware of its responsibilities to its citizens to minimize any resultant human hardship,

> NOW THEREFORE BE IT RESOLVED that New York State hereby advocates a positive program to stimulate automation equipment manufacture in the state and to encourage the adoption of automated methods and equipment by businesses and industries within the state.

> ALSO BE IT RESOLVED, in order to foster an environment free of fear and conducive to such development, that New York State immediately establish an advisory group on automation. This group is to include representatives of labor, management, and the general public as well as the state Departments of Labor, Commerce, Education, and Finance. This body is to develop a framework of objectives and policies that will make it possible for the state to reap the full benefits of new technology, and at the same time minimize any human hardship.

As a first step, the advisory group is hereby empowered to mount a program of trial case studies to obtain the necessary facts regarding the economic consequences of automation to New York State.

Chapter 10

AT THE NATIONAL LEVEL

> *Essential to a program of national action on automation and related technology is a solid factual foundation on which to base public policy. Legislation cannot be effective if it is devised in a factual vacuum. A meaningful study of the subject must be broad enough in scope to cover all pertinent aspects. It should include industry case studies on the introduction of automated equipment and what the consequences were. And it should include a substantial body of information elicited on a broad basis through detailed questionnaires.*

This Chapter is based on the report by John Diebold, "Automation: Its Impact on Business and Labor," prepared for the National Planning Association, Washington, D.C., published as Planning Pamphlet No. 106, copyright, May, 1959.

Automation has become something that everybody wants to "do something about." There are many theories about what should be done. However, there are few facts about automation, and as yet, there is still no systematic way of thinking about its economic and social consequences. This is a very dangerous situation for the nation. The United States is very close to the point of formulating national policy based on conjecture and myth. It may be a question of national survival, and this country should find out what can *really* be expected from automation.

There is an obvious need for factual information and for a proper framework within which to evaluate these facts. National policy should not be set by the group that shouts the loudest. In considering a national policy for automation, it may be well to review first some of the basic conflicts in points of view on the subject.

ECONOMIC CONSEQUENCES

The fundamental question about all new technology is: where and how fast? Like mass production, automation is not simply the growth of a new industry, but rather a "horizontal" advance of technology across industry lines that will affect not one segment of the economy but many. No dissenting voice has been raised to question the proposition that in the long run this technology will have beneficial economic and social effects as significant as the effects of the technological advances of the last century. But many fear that there will be serious dislocation and hardship during the transition period.

The key to the economic impact of automation is the rate of speed at which it is introduced. If the changes of the last fifty years had been compressed into two or three years, economic chaos would have resulted. If the changes automation will bring would take place overnight, there would be cause for real concern. The crucial first question for a study of the consequences of this new technology, therefore, is how far and how fast it will go.

Some observers contend that automation and its related technology will have more in common with a glacier than a flood. It will go far in the end but, in their view, there is not much chance that it will sweep ahead so fast that it will swamp the economy. There are a number of factors they believe will tend to slow its spread.

Not Everything Can Be Automated

Even those industries that are most ripe for automation will probably never become completely automated. The manless factory is a technical possibility, but there are good reasons for thinking that it will never be built.

Dr. Cledo Brunetti, when Director of Engineering Research and Development at General Mills, pointed out, for example, that the automated part of an electronics assembly plant so far is strictly limited. It "cannot buy components, cannot receive them, cannot inspect and test them nor deliver them to the production floor. It cannot even assemble components having odd shapes. . . . The machine cannot put in tubes, align and test the final assembly, put it in the cabinet or attach knobs, dials, and decorative effects. It does not pack the final product, does not ship it, and certainly does not market the product."

Right now, machines could be built to perform some of these operations, but there is often a great gap between what is technically possible and what is economically practical. Plymouth has automated the assembly of V-8 engines by installing a three-section transfer machine with 198 stations. About 100 people work on this line. According to Vice-president Ralph E. Cross of the Cross Company, which designed and built the machine, the number of workers could probably be cut in half if the line were made as automatic as present technology permits. However, the cost of the engine would go up, because on some of the stations it is cheaper to use conventional assembly methods than to automate. Similarly, a Ford official has said that he foresees only limited application of automation in assembly plants, which employ about 30 per cent of the company's total work force, because of both technical barriers and the fact that body structure and trim design change so frequently. It is hard to know whether or not this will be the case in five or ten years, when flexible assembly equipment may well be in existence.

The High Cost

This may well turn out to be the highest hurdle in the path of rapid automation. Plymouth's automatic assembly machines cost $2.5 million. Ford's first automated cylinder block line cost nearly $9 million, 25 per cent more than a conventional line, although costs have since been somewhat lowered by the use of standardized elements. The capital investment per worker in the highly automated ammonia industry is $42,500, more than three times as high as the comparable figure for all manufacturing industries. The price tag on an Autofab reads $160,000, and on a large electronic computer something in the neighborhood of $2.5

million, and often much higher. Smaller machines are beginning to appear, but they are still expensive. The costs of conversion alone are as high as the costs of the equipment itself.

Occasionally, to be sure, new automatic equipment costs less than replacing existing equipment. A transfer machine to machine axle housings can replace, at a cost of $318,000, five separate machines with a total replacement cost of $540,000. But the transfer machine has to be installed and paid for all at once, while conventional machines can be replaced one at a time as they wear out. Even in cases like this, therefore, automation of this type is likely to be limited to companies with large financial resources.

Manpower Shortage

The shortage of technical manpower is a severe limitation on the speedy introduction of automation. Although accredited technical colleges are increasing the sizes of their graduating classes each year, the figure is still far below the number required to fill even current needs adequately. Engineers are in such demand that it is not unusual for graduates of an engineering school to receive an average of seven job offers apiece. Several large companies have advertised their willingness to hire the entire graduating class of some engineering schools, sight unseen. Not only engineers, but machinists, toolmakers, draftsmen, machine assemblers, skilled maintenance men, and repairmen are in serious short supply.

Elmer C. Easton, Dean of the College of Engineering of Rutgers University, testified before a Congressional hearing on automation that "there should be three to five technicians for every engineer. Although exact information is lacking, it is probable that the average ratio is one to one in the United States at present." It has been estimated that each year we fall short of our requirements by 25,000 engineers and 75,000 technicians. Automation will increase the demand for these men.

It is obvious that this shortage of skilled manpower is a brake on the progress of automation. Skilled labor is necessary not only for the design of automatic equipment, but also for its introduction, operation, and maintenance. A business will not invest in the new equipment without the assurance that there will be adequate help to run it. New technology will advance only as fast as the necessary multiplication of skills paves the way for it. ❭

Automating Is a Long Term Process

Automation is far more than simply buying an elaborate new machine and plugging it in. Months, sometimes years, of work may go into planning automatic processes and designing and building the specialized machines. For example, the Carborundum Company, which manufactures sandpaper and other coated abrasives, has begun to use radioisotope gauges for automatic process control, but four years elapsed between the time when the idea was seriously considered and the time when the gauges were actually installed on a manufacturing machine on a trial basis.

Even before management can think about how to design and build the machines, it must be willing—and able—to do the boldest kind of thinking about company operations. Must the product retain its present shape? Can the process be restructured to allow more continuous production? How much existing equipment could be used in an automated unit? Will it be cheaper to buy standard equipment and adapt it, or to have special equipment designed? What will the new equipment do to space requirements? What will it mean in the way of personnel changes? How will production changes affect markets? These questions and many more like them are difficult to answer, but it may be even more difficult for management to ask them in the first place. Men who have spent many years in a business are often quite honestly incapable of looking at product and process in a fresh light without considerable aid from the outsider.

Moreover, as the *Harvard Business Review* once noted, "It is not easy to try to think of ways to make millions of dollars worth of equipment obsolete—especially when the funds are not readily available." Furthermore, it is no help that military secrecy and the great complexities of the new techniques have caused management understanding of business applications to lag behind technical development.

The experience of the Dixie Cup Company gives some idea of what is involved in automating a plant. Dixie is by no means completely automated, but it has, over a period of years, made large-scale production changes with an eye to offsetting rising labor and raw materials costs by increasing efficiency. In the course of making the changes, more than 75 per cent of its manufacturing equipment was moved. "We have taken entire departments and transferred them, not a few feet but up or down a floor in our multi-story plant," J. W. Kuebler, vice-president in charge of production, has explained. He added that "Air, vacuum, steam, water and liquid-wax systems have all been revised to conform to our new layouts. We have moved offices, and in one instance we found it desirable to eliminate a stairway between two floors. We have . . . taken departments that were formerly considered to be entirely separate, even to the extent of supervision, and combined them to give us continuity of operation."

These are some of the reasons that have been put forth to show that automation will not come with devastating speed. Until now, however, they are indications only, not backed by solid, factual knowledge.

THE FLOOD

The opinion that the introduction of new technology will be sufficiently slow and restrained so as not to play havoc with the economy is not unanimous. Labor leaders in particular have expressed grave fears that it will come fast, go far, and bring serious problems with it. "We are just beginning to get our big toe wet in the field of automation," Walter Reuther has said. "When we wade in up to our knees the impact will be tremendous; when we get up to our Adam's apple, it will be much greater." In this view, the following important indicators show that the level of automation is fast rising to flood proportions.

Sales of Equipment Are Booming

One indicator is the rate of spending for automated equipment. There is no doubt that it has increased rapidly in the last few years. As pointed out in Chapter 2, the automation equipment industry, which scarcely existed at the end of the war, grew to a $3 billion industry in 1954, and by 1962 the industry had reached over $7 billion. Spending for control instruments rose from $3 million in 1940 to $65 million by

1953, and is expected to reach $250 million by 1967. IBM alone is already shipping more than one medium-sized computer a day, and predicts that there will be 10,000 large digital computers in business use by 1965.

After viewing figures like these, one labor union predicted that if this upward trend continues, American industry may be fully automated within this decade.

The Possibilities of Automation

There is some tendency to treat those industries in which automation is not likely to play a major role as if they did not exist at all. Yet it is the total impact of automation on the economy that will count, and even industries not susceptible to a high level of automation will, if they automate at all, make some contribution to the total.

Transportation, for example, usually appears high on any list of industries in which automation does not appear to have much future. However, in addition to making extensive use of computers, several railroads have already constructed automated yards for the handling and dispatching of freight cars. Cars are automatically switched to the proper classification tracks in these yards. After track selections are fed into the system, human action is seldom needed. Where yardmen used to ride the tops of cars, retarding them with brake clubs as they shunted into classification tracks, now a single retarder operator in a control tower watches a control panel, intervening only in case of emergency. The Seaboard Air Line Railroad's 58-track automated yard at Hamlet, North Carolina, can hump more cars in eight hours than a conventional yard can hump in twenty-four. In any case, in a field as rapidly moving as this one, it may not be wise to take anything for granted.

Savings Can Offset High Costs

The disadvantage of expensive equipment may be more than canceled out by the tremendous savings that automation makes possible. For example, the Pennsylvania Railroad estimated that it would recoup nearly the entire cost of its $34 million automated classification yard at Conway, Pennsylvania, in three years, since the yard was designed to pare $11 million from yearly operation expenses.

Direct labor savings alone may be very large in automated operations. At Ford's automated engine plant, nine workers at three machines are drilling the oil holes in the crankshafts, as against 39 workers at 39 machines in a conventional plant. The introduction of the printed circuit at the Philco plant in Sandusky, Ohio, reduced by 25 per cent the number of workers needed on the soldering and wiring assembly line. *Time* reported Charles Hautau's claim that he can cut a man off the payroll for every $5,000 a manufacturer invests in his automated machinery.

These savings may be partly canceled out by the need for more maintenance workers and the higher wages paid for higher skills. Even so, automation can cut costs in other less obvious directions. A Department of Labor study of an insurance company, which installed a computer in the classification sections of one of its divisions, reveals where some of these savings lie. The computer reduced personnel in this particular area from 198 to 85 workers and freed more than 15,000 square feet of floor space for other uses. It reduced the number of punched-card machines from 125 to 21, and the yearly rental for these machines from \$235,000 to \$19,000. Monthly punch card requirements have been cut by nearly 2.5 million. Altogether, the computer is expected to cut the classification sections' budgets in half.

Even the initial cost of automating, according to Wassily Leontief, professor of economics at Harvard, is not so high as is generally supposed. The cost of complete instrumentation of a new modern plant to make it as fully automatic as possible varies from industry to industry, but the average for all industries, he estimated in *Scientific American*'s symposium on automatic control, would be only about 6 per cent of the total cost of the plant. Six per cent, Professor Leontief argues, is far from a formidable figure, especially since "the smoother and better-balanced operation of self-regulating plants has already shown that they can function with less capitalization than a nonautomatic plant of identical capacity." The mechanization of the nineteenth century, he concludes, required heavy capital investment and proceeded slowly; the new technology, unhampered by such vast capital requirements, can be introduced at a much faster pace. It is only fair to add, however, that this view is seriously challenged by more recent observers who predict that 20 to 30 per cent of the cost of future process plants will be accounted for by highly elaborate control systems.

IMPACT ON INDUSTRY

The speed and extent of automation will greatly influence its economic effects. What these effects will be is the subject of heated discussion based on divergent opinions. Most of the discussion centers around what will happen to employment and what will happen to the worker. In addition to the broad effects on the overall employment and economic situation, automation will influence the structure of business and the task of management. Here, too, there are arguments concerning what this effect will be, and again, there are few facts to back up either side. The three areas which receive the most attention in this context are the effects of new technology on the size of business, on competition, and on management.

The Size of Business

Will the advent of automation and related information technology give companies that are already big such an overwhelming advantage that small and medium-sized business will be forced to the wall? At present, the condition of small business is causing considerable alarm in some quarters. Net growth in the number of business firms has increased very slightly. Small business failures have remained high, and small business sales and profits have lagged far behind those of big business.

How will automation affect this picture? Since small business usually does not have either large amounts of money to invest in new plant and equipment or a volume of production and sales that would justify spending the money even if it were available, it would seem that automation, because of its high costs, might spell the doom of all but the industrial giants.

The prospect for small business, however, is not necessarily a gloomy one. There are a number of ways in which costs can be brought within the reach of companies that cannot afford to invest hundreds of thousands of dollars in machines. Rental of capital equipment is already common, particularly in the case of computers. Businesses can now rent smaller computers for $2,000 to $3,000 a month. Flexible machine tools will give small shops and factories the advantages of automatic operation without large investments in capital equipment. Some equipment is already being specially designed with small business in mind.

Moreover, small business may have an advantage for the very reason that it will not be geared to extremely long runs of standardized products. The difficulty and cost of making changes may tend to make the large, highly automated plants rigid and monolithic. A small business, by reason of its greater flexibility and lower overhead, can, as one observer has noted, develop a new product and have it on the market "before the highly automated plant can even draw plans."

Automation, as it is commonly conceived by those who do not fully comprehend its possibilities, can significantly decrease the flexibility of the large company. The type of automation that requires huge investment in tooling and machinery before anything is produced will prevent some large companies from moving in quickly to take advantage of shifts in demand or new developments. The necessity of running large quantities of the same item before the investment is recovered will force many large, inflexibly automated firms to give up certain areas of the market where runs are small and where variety is required for success. Such tendencies are already visible in an industrial structure influenced by assembly line production.

On the other hand, true automation does not necessarily mean long runs of standardized products. Technical advances may bring flexibility to some of the larger-scale manufacturing processes. Further, advantages that come with size but are not related to scale production will continue to assist the large companies. Such advantages include the large company's ability to advertise and make major capital investments. As usual, there are arguments for both points of view, and that is all the more reason that a real attempt should be made to get as much factual information as possible.

Competition

In an industry where competition is strong, introduction of new equipment is likely to proceed quickly because there is heavy pressure on individual firms to cut their costs. If there is little competition, the pressure for improvements will be less. Competitors who fail to use advanced techniques may be forced out of business while more progressive firms or new entrants into the industry may expand. Important in any consideration of the effects of automation on competition is the availability of technical knowledge required for automatic production and the ability of competitors to use the latest technology. The role of patents must be carefully studied to determine whether the tools of the new technology are accessible to all.

Management

New technology presents a unique challenge to management, not only to perform old tasks better, but to reach new levels of achievement and to change further and enhance the role of the professional manager. To embark on a program of automation, management must have the imagination, insight, and courage to make sweeping changes that are certain to be expensive. Automation creates some jobs that only technicians can do. But as pointed out in Chapter 4, management, too, has a role in automation which is perhaps even more complex and difficult. It must have the imagination to rethink the problems of an entire business in terms of ultimate goal and final product.

So far, the record has only been fair, but a major problem —recognition of the magnitude of the problem—may have been overcome.

Employment

The most vocal and passionate arguments concern the effects of automation on employment—or on unemployment. Mixtures of economic theory, social philosophy, historical determinism, and statistical juggling are used in discussions, but there is still a great shortage of facts.

Will total job opportunities increase or decrease as a result of the new technology? It is a matter of historical record that over a period of time there have been employment opportunities for those displaced through economic change. But as Sylvania's Chairman, Don G. Mitchell, has pointed out, "It doesn't do much good to try to convince an individual worker who does get displaced from an individual job that over a 25-year span there is no such thing as technological unemployment. He doesn't care whether there is or not. All he is worried about is that he lost a job." That workers themselves are worried, rightly or wrongly, is indicated by a radio poll conducted a few years ago in Detroit which reported that, next to Russia, what frightened people most was automation.

The mainstay of fear and confusion is ignorance, and

much of the unrest is caused more by uncertainty than by any knowledge that automation will be harmful. Such fear and unrest can give rise to policies and actions that may have a detrimental long-term effect on the development and progress of the United States economy. All these signs are simply further indications of the need to find out the facts.

Plenty of jobs for everyone? Many believe that displacement is not now a serious problem and that it is not likely to become one. Even a highly automated operation needs workers, although they will not be doing the same jobs they did before. There are good reasons for believing that automation in practice has had more of a tendency to create jobs than to do away with them.

For one thing, automation has created one whole new and booming industry—the industry that produces automation equipment. Already, the number of firms engaged either wholly or partly in the manufacture of automatic control equipment numbers well over a thousand. One of the fastest growing industry groups in the nation is the instruments and related products field, in which employment has more than tripled since 1939.

Perhaps even more significant is the fact that automation makes it possible to do many things that could not be done without it, in both factories and offices, and the new goods and services that result provide increased job opportunities. It is impossible to anticipate all the industries that will develop from this new technology, but some of them already exist or can be anticipated. The entire atomic energy industry, present and future, rests on automation, for no human could operate valves or hand controls within an atomic reactor and live. Polyethylene, the flexible plastic widely used for packaging and for squeeze bottles, cannot be made without automation. Color television, at a price that can attract a large market, depends on automatic machines to lay on the picture tube the hundreds of thousands of accurately spaced colored dots. Chemists believe the chemical industry may be revolutionized by the use of high-speed computers to control reactions far too fast for human control. Ralph Cordiner speaks of a transistor and semiconductor industry, an industry for the production of supermetals like titanium and zirconium, and even an industry for producing man-made diamonds. "Every time you build an automatic machine," one enthusiastic industrialist has summed up, "the thing opens up new vistas of things you can do with it and products that you can make available that you never dreamed of before."

Moreover, there has been a long term trend toward increasing employment in the service industries. Between 1900 and 1950, employment in these industries increased 6.1 times —nearly three times as much as the increase in total employment during this period. In 1962 41.2 per cent of the gross national product was spent on purchase of services. If automation, by increasing productivity, brings rising incomes and greater leisure, the labor displaced in manufacturing may find a wealth of new openings in the service industries.

Some even doubt that any "displaced" labor will develop. The rate at which the labor supply is increasing is not keeping pace with increases in the demand for labor. Within the next twenty years industry will be facing not a labor surplus but a potential labor shortage. The working population is substantially composed of people between the ages of 20 and 65. All those who will be in this category in 20 years have already been born. The age of retirement is dropping; the age of those entering the labor force is rising, because of the increasing proportion of young people attending college or serving in the military forces and therefore entering the labor market later. These trends and some others—for example, the increase in the number of women in the child-bearing age group, of whom relatively few will work—indicate that the labor force in 1975 will probably range between 78 and 86 millions.

The demand for labor will in all probability exceed this supply. The standard of living has increased since 1940 at an annual rate of 2.65 per cent. Even if this rate of increase is just maintained, the gross national product in 1975 will be approximately $858 billion measured in 1955 dollars. Something like 84 million workers will be needed to turn out this quantity of goods and services if productivity maintains its average annual increase of 2.45 per cent and if the average work week remains unchanged.

Labor leaders have already announced that their next goal after the guaranteed annual wage will be a four-day work week. If this goal is achieved by 1975, industry will need the equivalent of an additional 21 million workers— 25 per cent more than 84 million—to turn out the volume of goods and services that 84 million workers could produce in a five-day week. Since there will not be this many workers, even by the most sanguine estimates, automation represents the key to the problem. By greatly increasing productivity, it will make the potential labor shortage less acute.

Or, not enough work to go around? For both passion and volume, the arguments that paint automation as something

to be feared—or at least controlled—are in the lead. There
are many sound bases to these arguments, and they may well
represent a realistic point of view. Those who point out the
dangers of automation are deeply concerned that over the
next five to ten years, when they expect the great changes
to come, there will be a surplus not of jobs but of job-seekers.

According to Census Bureau estimates, the average annual
increase in the labor force is at present 700,000 to 800,000.
By 1965, it will rise to more than 1 million. Job opportunities
must open up for all these people, as well as for any others
who are displaced because of productivity increases. Walter
Reuther has pointed out that the economy is burdened with
the responsibility of providing over three million new job
opportunities a year, when productivity rises 4 per cent and
the labor force increases by some 700,000. Increases in
productivity plus increases in the labor force will demand
a substantial number of new job opportunities every year.

Moreover, as one union official has noted, the need for
goods and services and the actual purchase of goods and
services may be two quite different things, as they were in
the 1930s, when the needs were great and the purchases
small. He says: "Needs in themselves do not produce customers; rather it is needs backed up with cash or credit."
Unless markets continue to grow because purchasing power
is growing, the whole argument that there will be more jobs
than there will be workers to fill them falls apart.

Unemployment figures would seem to indicate that no
large number of workers has as yet been displaced by automation. Yet at least one observer, Warner Bloomberg, Jr.,
of the University of Chicago, has suggested that even this
low figure can mask a considerable amount of displacement.

He believes that even today "an uncounted number of industrial and office workers—more than likely going in the hundreds of thousands—are 'temporarily out of work' because the devices of the new technology have taken over their functions." Since there is no real difficulty in most areas in finding some kind of job, they take what they can get and are no longer unemployed. In the process of making the shift, however, these workers may lose seniority rights, insurance, pensions, and other benefits, and may have had to settle for a less congenial job at lower wages as well.

Although there have been no mass layoffs because of automation, there is concern in some quarters that jobs are vanishing. Many of the industrialists who testified before the Congressional subcommittee said that one way they absorbed workers displaced by machines was to shift them into positions vacated by employees who left the company's employ for reasons not connected with automation. "The worker displaced is not fired," Professor Walter S. Buckingham of the Georgia Institute of Technology has said, "he is the one who is not hired." As automation spreads, and particularly as small and medium-sized businesses find a way to make their production and office procedures at least partly automatic, more and more of the routine jobs that now employ millions of workers will be handled by machines. Many contend that the true impact of automation will only be seen when it grows to the point where normal turnover can no longer disguise its effects.

As for the new opportunities for employment in new industries or in old ones that are expanding, a worker can take advantage of them only if he is where the jobs are. Over the long pull, United States labor is highly mobile, but individual workers are not always easily uprooted. Social legislation in the last decades has even reduced the need for individual mobility. Family responsibility, financial obligations, or simply inertia make it difficult for many workers to pick up and look for a job in another location. This is especially true for older workers who have spent a lifetime in a community, and it is these older workers who may be hardest hit by technological displacement. Even younger workers may need help in meeting the financial costs of relocating and retraining.

Those who fear that automation will not create jobs as fast as it destroys them believe that not only individuals but entire communities may be bypassed by the march of progress if automation makes it cheaper for industries to build whole new plants than to remodel existing ones. Since the need for labor will not be so great, these plants can move away from areas where the labor supply is large; and as nuclear power develops, they will no longer be tied to existing power sources. If this should turn out to be the case, whole communities may need assistance if their inhabitants are not to become victims of the age of automation.

SOCIAL CONSEQUENCES

Automation's social consequences are broader than its economic effects. Results in the social sphere also depend on the speed and degree of automation. Although automation can influence nearly every phase of our lives, there is as great a lack of factual information in this area as there is for the economic questions. A consideration of some of the major issues can do little more than illustrate the need for more knowledge.

Effect on the Nature of Jobs

Upgrading or Downgrading. In at least one respect, the changes automation will bring to labor are all to the good. Norbert Wiener has said that the "human machine" is too complicated for such tasks as pasting labels on tin cans, or sorting and packing spears of asparagus, or tightening one or two bolts on a car on an assembly line; and that "it is degradation to a human being to chain him to an oar and use him as a source of power; but it is an almost equal degradation to assign him a purely repetitive task in a factory which demands less than a millionth of his brain capacity."

These are the very jobs that machines will take over in an automated factory or office. Considerably fewer workers will be needed for routine, monotonous jobs because machines will be doing that work. The jobs that will be reserved for people are those requiring judgment and those that a machine cannot readily be built to do—in other words, the more interesting ones.

The new jobs will call for less use of muscles and more use of judgment, since automatic machines are delicate and complex and call for a high level of skill and precision on the part of their human monitors. Supervising an automatic machine may be a highly skilled job, although it calls for no more physical exertion than pushing a button or changing a setting on a controller. Professor Thomas J. Walsh of the Case Institute of Technology points this up with a story of a test on a new refinery unit designed to produce 15,000 barrels of aviation gasoline a day. From early morning until the middle of the afternoon on the day of the test, an operator and a crew of four men worked at the controls, and by 3 o'clock had managed to raise the rate of production from 15,000 barrels to 18,500. At that point, a new operator came on, and said, "Well, we can do more than that." Professor Walsh reported: "In about half an hour he pushed it to 23,500 and said, 'Boy, that is as far as you are going to go.'" To change the one particular setting on the one particular control that did the job, he had to evaluate the operations of all the instruments ranged in three tiers on three sides of a good-sized room.

Some workers themselves have testified that they like the new jobs better than their old ones. A. H. Raskin, after a visit to Ford's River Rouge Plant, reported that workers on the automated line "go home less tired; the pay is better; the work is softer. Few complain of boredom. On the contrary, they speak of their mechanical charges with a pride that is rare among factory workers." A foreman who supervises twenty-one men on a block of automated boring machines told him: "The men are more cheerful, and that means a lot less heartache getting the work out. In the old days, I used to write a man up five or six times a week for violating company rules. Now I don't think I wrote a man up all year. It's 90 per cent of your battle if you have contented men." This is, of course, not a universal reaction.

Even if the new jobs will be better jobs, this does not answer the two questions uppermost in the thinking of most workers and labor leaders: who will fill the new jobs? And will there be enough of these better jobs to go around?

The very fact that the new jobs demand higher skills creates problems. Since the need for unskilled labor will decline and the need for skilled and semiskilled technicians will grow, automation brings with it the possibility of a distinct upgrading of jobs. "The hand trucker of today replaced by a conveyor belt might become tomorrow's electronic engineer," as one industrialist put it.

However, upgrading of jobs is not the same thing as upgrading of particular workers, as the case of Stanley Tylak indicates. Tylak, aged 61, for twenty-seven years a job setter at Ford, was shifted to the automated engine plant and found that he could not cope with his new responsibilities. "The machines had about 80 drills and 22 blocks going through," he told a reporter from the New York *Post*. "You had to watch all the time. Every few minutes you had to watch to see everything was all right. And the machines had so many lights and switches—about 90 lights. It sure is hard on your mind. If there's a break in the machine the whole line breaks down. But sometimes you make a little mistake, and it's no good for you, no good for the foreman, no good for the company, no good for the union." Stanley Tylak was shifted to another job at lower pay. He was downgraded, not upgraded.

In most cases, however, the new skills are well within the ability of today's assembly line and office workers. Even the advanced level of working with a computer is not beyond the capabilities of existing office staffs. The Census Bureau, which pioneered in the use of computers for office work, found that in a matter of a few months people already on its staff were able to learn programming. "The important ingredient to success," one employee of the Bureau stated, "is not learning how to program for the equipment, but knowing and understanding the problem."

The Problem of Retraining. Workers will not automatically fit into new jobs. Unskilled workers, workers with specialized skills whose jobs have been taken over by machines, and older workers who have spent a working lifetime in a job only to find their skills made obsolete overnight, all have to be retrained so that they have a chance to acquire the new skills they need to work in an automated factory or office. Older workers, skilled or unskilled, present a particular problem. It is not easy for them to learn a new skill or, since employers are notably reluctant to hire them, to find a new job.

So far, with automation only in its infancy, many of the industries that have installed automatic machinery have successfully retrained or transferred to other spots in the company all the workers whose jobs have evaporated with the installation of the machines. Indeed, Ralph E. Cross has stated categorically that over a period of years he has witnessed the installation of thousands of automated machines "and during this time I have never seen where the installation of a new machine has caused workers to be laid off or discharged. I don't know of any company that does not retrain its workers to new jobs when changes are required by new products or new processes."

It is encouraging that industry itself is alert to the problem and to its responsibilities. It is also encouraging that other institutions have begun to take steps to train both those who are already in the working force and those who will one day join it for the new jobs that automation creates. Several universities, for example, are now offering courses in computer programming, and a number of computer manufacturers are training clerical personnel on the job. A technical high school in Buffalo offers a course in which students build a digital computer and then learn to solve problems with it.

The spread of automation, however, will call for training and retraining on a much broader scale. "Many of today's electricians will have to learn electronics if they are to retain their skilled status," according to the National Manpower Council. "Pipefitters may have to learn hydraulics. A skilled worker who formerly measured with calipers and now uses a micrometer will soon have to learn to work with tolerances measured with light waves. . . . There may be almost no place left for the unskilled industrial worker."

The problem of who is going to do all the training and how it is going to be done therefore raises important policy questions, which so far have scarcely been asked and have not begun to be answered. On whom should the burden fall? On the community? On the firm? On the worker? What new kinds of educational programs are needed, and where? Are the high schools giving the kind of commercial and vocational training that will be needed? Or are they teaching skills that will be outmoded before they can be used? These questions can only be answered after a study shows what skills have been made obsolete, what new skills will be needed, and how soon they are likely to be needed.

Broader Social Implications

The questions automation raises for society as a whole go far beyond the problems of what it will mean for industry and labor. Consumers will probably find that many of the things they buy will be cheaper and of better quality. Will they also be more standardized? "Many different models are possible from combining a few standardized processes in different ways," Professor Buckingham has observed, "but, as in automobiles, the final products are still likely to look pretty much alike." Others, however, have suggested that it is perhaps because the products of Detroit look pretty much all alike that foreign cars, which look different, have found a market in the United States. There may be a limit beyond which standardization—and consumers—cannot be pushed. It is not, after all, the machine that decides what man shall have.

More important is the question of increasing leisure. Many observers believe that machines will soon provide a choice between added products and comforts and added leisure. If leisure becomes the choice, it is entirely possible that the three-day weekend, or the three-month vacation, will be a reality within the next decade. While a major sociological study would be required to deal fully with the implications of additional leisure, some of them can at least be suggested.

For one thing, leisure is sure to change patterns of consumption. As we have indicated in earlier chapters, people with more time off will spend more money on sports clothes and equipment, on hobbies, on travel and its adjuncts. The already booming do-it-yourself movement is certain to boom even further. Americans have the reputation of being a nation of joiners. It seems likely that the number and size of fraternal and community organizations will grow as more free time becomes available.

But additional leisure may also have more subtle and perhaps less favorable effects. Some observers, like Erich Fromm, feel that increasing man's leisure tends only to increase his sense of insecurity. Too much time may isolate him psychologically, create problems which he is unprepared to face, and drive him to socially harmful actions. And David Riesman contends that many Americans look on additional leisure as "a threat, a problem, a burden, or hazard."

The report of one Congressional subcommittee suggests that even the choice between more goods and more leisure involves "something of an ethical challenge," for in this country there still are "substantial groups of comparatively underprivileged and lower income groups who should be remembered before those in the more favored industries can conscientiously turn to a shortened work day or longer weekend."

Sooner or later, it is clear, however, society will have to face the question: Is this country capable of developing a culture that does not depend on work to give meaning to our lives?

To illustrate the divergence of opinions on the effects of automation, a list of pertinent arguments might be helpful. It should be remembered that these points of view are argued with a vehemence that varies in inverse proportion to the facts available.

The Pleasant Side of Automation

1. Automation is nothing new, so there is no reason for concern. Technological changes have occurred throughout history without dire results, and automation is just another technological change. There is no more need to legislate against automation than there was need to slow down the introduction of the assembly line. Technological change is progress and should be welcomed.

2. Everything will work out in the long run. The natural

forces in the economy will make whatever adjustments may be necessary to the introduction of automation. This can be brought about through the movement of displaced workers to other industries, through the expansion of output of industries that automate, or through the introduction of new industries into the economy. If the industries that apply automation expand their output, there may be the need for the same number of workers, but they will be producing a great deal more than before. The introduction of new industries, through invention and research, will take up whatever slack may develop in the economy.

3. Automation is the key to a shorter work week. There is an unmistakable trend toward less work and more leisure. To realize this goal without sacrificing our real standard of living it is necessary to increase productivity. Automation is the means to increase it. The result of automation will not be forced idleness or unemployment but the enjoyment of more leisure.

4. Unlimited demand for goods and services will prevent unemployment. Since human wants are unlimited, increased productivity and production through automation will find a market in satisfying these wants. Through greater productivity, earnings will increase to such an extent that there will be a tremendous rise in the standard of living. These increased earnings can come about through higher wages or through lower prices, or through a combination of the two. This argument does not imply that everybody will have to be convinced of the need for a third car. What it means is that as demand for a certain article is satisfied, new demands will arise. As the refrigerator market became saturated, the air conditioner and dishwasher were developed.

5. Automation will create a bigger pie, so that everybody's slice will be larger. This is far better than trying to limit the size of the overall pie and then fighting about how the smaller pie is to be distributed.

6. Automation will come slowly and in limited quantity. It is neither big enough nor fast enough to warrant concern. Its speed is limited by the long-range planning it requires, the shortage of trained personnel, and the huge investment required. At best, it will affect only a small segment of the total economy, and even those who are so affected will have plenty of time to adjust.

7. Automation is the only means of maintaining our standard of living in the face of a significant labor shortage. The future problem will be unavailability of labor, not unavailability of jobs.

8. Employment has been increasing. While everybody is shouting about the harmful effects of automation on employment, there has been a steady increase in employment in the past few years during which the impact of automation should have been at its highest.

9. Automation brings about lower prices. This is a variation of the thesis that automation helps a company expand and thus enables it to absorb or retain the people who might otherwise have been replaced by automation. As prices go down, given an elastic demand situation, the demand for the product will increase and output will also increase. Luxury articles will attain wider distribution, living standards will go up, and there will be work for all. If the increased productivity is not reflected in lower prices—or in the same price for a better product—then it will be reflected in higher wages. Higher wages will have the same effect.

10. A more responsible management will not permit automation to have harmful effects on employment. Today, management has a social responsibility. As a result management itself will control the introduction of automation into its business so that no hardships are created, or so that hardships are minimized. Closely related to such social consciousness are programs of retraining and transferring workers to other operations in the same company.

11. Development and growth may occasionally mean hardship, but it is a small price to pay for progress. This is a rare argument, but as an attitude it may be more prevalent. It is similar to the contention that the best solution for economic hardship is to produce the biggest pie possible. In many cases, nonmaterial concepts are also brought out. Freedom of the individual to innovate and create is considered one of mankind's accomplishments on which no limits should be set.

12. The growth of the automation industry itself will provide employment for a good number of those put out of work by the products of the automation industry.

13. Automation is the key to national survival. The only way that the United States will be able to stay ahead of, or keep pace with, Russia is through a strenuous increase in productivity. More leisure, more comfort, and more consumption goods are the goals of American economic policy. A shorter work week is a reality that the economy will have to face in the next few years. At the same time, this country is engaged in a race for economic and military supremacy with a nation that is devoted to hard work, individual privation for the sake of future strength, and gigantic efforts toward increased productivity and production.

14. Automation will bring economic stability. In an auto-

mated plant, labor costs will be so low and capital costs so high that it will pay to continue production and lower prices rather than to cut production and lay people off. Even if production is cut, the cut in employment will not be proportionate because most of the work will be indirect labor that does not vary with volume of production. Furthermore, automation programs must be long-term in nature, and their completion will not depend on short-term changes in sales. This means that investment expenditures will be more stable. In these ways, cyclical fluctuations will be reduced.

The Unpleasant Side

Hardly anybody is against automation; as a matter of fact, nearly everybody is for it, because it is a word that implies "progress." Predictions of dire consequences from automation usually end with the warning that it must be controlled rather than stopped, and that countermeasures must be taken against its harmful effects. The more common arguments for concern over automation are indicated below.

1. An overall pattern of economic prosperity has helped up to now. The advent of automation—which is still in its infancy—has been accompanied by the greatest period of boom that America has ever experienced. Temporary recessions are cited as instances in which the economy could not keep pace with the employment dislocations of automation. Technological change is one of the causes of the cyclical unemployment. The real trouble will come when the rate of growth of the economy slows down, because there will be no means of absorbing those made idle through automation.

2. Automation is an accelerating phenomenon. Its real effects have not been demonstrated. The real impact will come in the future, when the gestation period is over, and the technical difficulties have been overcome. At that time, there will be a sudden surge forward, at an accelerating rate, and the resulting unemployment will wreak havoc with the economy. When current technical limitations are overcome, companies will automate to reduce their costs. Other companies will be forced to imitate in order to remain competitive. Thus the impact will go from company to company and industry to industry like a row of falling dominoes. At that time, all the factors that have up to now limited automation's impact will be swept aside by the pressure of costs and competition. It is foolish to look to the past to determine whether automation should be controlled, because the past does not show us the true face and power of automation.

3. There will be no purchasing power. As new machines replace workers and permit the manufacture of products without labor, these workers will be unemployed. As a result, they will not be receiving the wages that permit them to buy the products of American industry. The result will be the piling up of stocks in warehouses and the biggest depression ever experienced. Like every depression, it will spread to those areas of the economy that are not directly affected—the nonautomated areas.

This is an extremely powerful argument, and it is behind a great many of the measures designed to assure the flow of income to the people regardless of automation: the guaranteed annual wage, the shorter work week with equal pay, and a higher minimum wage. It is an outgrowth of the underconsumption theory of the business cycle, and it still has tremendous influence on economic thinking, even among some theoreticians.

4. Job opportunities cannot grow as fast as necessary. Those who fear automation point out that with productivity increasing at a rate of 4 per cent each year, and with 700,000 workers entering the labor market each year, there must be an increase in job opportunities of 3 million per year. The creation of so many job opportunities each year is practically impossible under present conditions, and the difficulty will become more and more severe as the rate of productivity increase continues.

5. Markets will become saturated. There is really no sense in pretending that automation will permit the same number of workers to turn out more products, because there will be no desire for these additional products. The truth is that there will be fewer workers turning out the same amount of products, because there is a certain point beyond which additional units will not be absorbed.

6. Automation means the subjugation of man by the machine.

On Balance

In comparing the pessimistic point of view with the optimistic, two things become clear. In the first place, the pessimistic side (those favoring control and mitigation) is much the more powerful. It is on the offensive and it has many more active advocates. It can appeal to the emotions much more effectively. Secondly, the pessimistic side has a definite program which it can champion. The higher minimum wage, the guaranteed annual wage, the four-day week, the granting of specific guarantees, and eventually, the control of investments in automation—these are all specific points that can be put forth as a constructive program to avoid the dire consequences that are predicted. The opponents of these viewpoints have nothing concrete to offer, and they are constantly on the defensive.

Guide to a Study of Automation in the U.S. Economy

Automation is only one of the many complex interlocking factors that shape the economy. While it may not be practicable or possible to study all of the factors that make up the economy, it is possible to make an industry-by-industry study of what automation has meant so far, and thus foresee with some certainty what it is likely to mean in the future. The potential impact of automation is such that it must be planned for. There is not as yet complete enough information to plan for the kind of action automation will require from industry, labor, and government. It is for the purpose of obtaining this type of information that an initial study of the economic consequences of automation should be undertaken.

In making a study of automation, emphatic attention should be given to the education problem in all its aspects— a problem that is a corollary to the economic one. The educational problem is perhaps the most challenging one to be faced as the age of automation advances. First it is necessary to determine what the economic direction is likely to be, and then meet it with reasonable human foresight.

Case Sampling

The most useful way of collecting, organizing, and analyzing the information necessary to a study of the effects of automation and its related technology is a detailed case-by-case approach to a number of specific industries that are representative of the several types of applications of automation practiced today. It would be valuable also to study a few typical industries where there is some especially interesting aspect to the way automation has been applied or has affected them. The following list should provide a good starting point.

The Automotive Industry. This industry has solved some immense problems in automating some of its processes, and illustrates well the kind of automation that has come to be called "Detroit automation." A study of the industry should develop useful information on how workers and working conditions are affected in factories which have learned how to handle long runs with specially designed automatic machinery.

Paper Manufacturing. This is a processing industry which is beginning to use feedback control systems. The effects of automation on labor here are likely to be slight, since there will probably not be much reduction in working force, but there are other interesting aspects to be studied. A change in the productivity of the capital equipment is one of these. In addition, the technical problems in this industry give a good deal of insight into the fundamental technical problems that must be overcome before automation can become complete in the processing industries. For example, present methods of measuring or testing paper consistency involve actually tearing the paper and letting water seep through it. If this area of the industry is to be effectively automated, this method, which is now an art, must be turned into a science.

Food Processing. This is one of the traditional automatic

machinery areas and would be an interesting study from the standpoint of determining whether there are really any differences between the social and economic effects of introducing the older style of automatic machinery and the newer developments.

Airframe Manufacture. Since production runs are very short and engineering changes are frequent, the airframe industry has many of the problems of job shop manufacturers, even though it is dominated by a few large companies. In a sense, it could be said that the airframe industry is pioneering in job shop automation. Appropriate case studies, therefore, could shed considerable light on the potential forms and the pace of job shop automation.

The airframe manufacturing industry is again worth studying because it relies heavily on computers for scientific calculation. There has probably been an enormous increase in employment as a result of these techniques and it would be important to see whether the situation in this area is applicable to the wider problem of employment opportunities. In addition, the aircraft industry is starting to use computers on a wide scale for office use. However, an even more valuable study could be made in this field with insurance companies, since this industry is already using computers and is certain to be one of the heaviest users of them in the future.

Oil and Chemical Processing. These industries are highly instrumented and have introduced a certain amount of centralized control. They would provide a valuable study of the relationship between manufacturing areas and the office in an industry where there is almost no labor directly involved in the manufacturing process. As more is learned about the use of computers, considerable change is bound to occur in this industry through automation, and it is an area which should be explored. It is also an industry where it is possible to measure the effects of automation over a considerable period of time. A case study could review what happened in the original shift from batch to continuous processing twenty odd years ago.

Electronic Assembly. This industry is interesting because the problem of considerable and continuous variation of the product is involved. The methods that are being used to attack this problem, and their effects on an industry that even today relies on an enormous amount of womanpower for production, would illuminate the problems of other industries faced with this kind of situation.

Office Automation. In this area, several kinds of studies might profitably be made. For example, it would be worthwhile to compare the approaches used by Sylvania, which has a large number of branches and a single computer center for all of them, and by Allstate Insurance or Prudential, which also have a large number of branches and are introducing computers into each of them.

It is also important to find out what will happen when medium-sized business introduces computers into the office. There are many cases where this has already been done, and one or two case studies of such businesses would be very worthwhile.

Nonbusiness Uses of Computers

One of the most far-reaching influences of automation may well be the use of computers for cultural and purely scientific applications. Their use in such tasks as tracing satellites and codifying the Bible has received much publicity. Their possible capacities for extending the frontiers of present knowledge may have a significant influence on education and on the direction of future research.

It would also be of value to make similar case studies of industries that have not yet automated to any significant degree. These studies could be less thorough, but their objective would be to determine the factors that limit automation. Clearer definition of these barriers would enable us to determine whether automation in these areas is merely a question of time or whether the present obstacles are permanent ones. Some industries that would be appropriate for study in this area are construction, transportation, small job shops, and companies producing custom goods.

Study Procedure

The following steps are suggested for conducting these case studies in each industry:

1. A general introductory survey of the particular industry should be made so that the study team can get a general idea of the kind of developments that have been taking place.

2. On the basis of this introductory survey, one or two specific companies should be selected for more intensive study. These companies should be typical of the industry in the sense that they are doing things which other companies could and probably will do; that is, they should not be uniquely large, in a particularly dominating position, or financially capable of doing things other companies in the industry could not afford. However, there should also be companies that either have done or are doing a good deal in

the automation field, and in this respect they may not be typical of their industry.

3. Before a detailed approach is made on the case study of the company, the study team should obtain general and background information on the history and development of the company.

4. The study team should conduct a pilot study which would include: interviews with key people; discussion with both the personnel department and the union about actual personnel shifts; discussion with manufacturing and planning departments about existing and planned changes; meeting with the controller's department about changes in data processing; and an estimate of the relationship of the company to the industry at large.

5. From study and analysis of the pilot study results, it should be possible to develop a plan for a more detailed study, including check lists and a carefully devised plan of action.

6. Based on the data that have been obtained, further observation and interviews should be undertaken. During this time, the study team should primarily observe what is happening. Individual workers, as well as members of management, should be interviewed and their observations studied in detail. All related files and interoffice memos should be examined and, during the course of the study, all pertinent interoffice data should be available to the study team. The team should plan to spend a substantial amount of time on the company's premises, since the more revealing findings may come from a study of a process in the course of development, even though a good deal may have been done toward automation. The team should attend meetings and talk

freely with people, but it is important that they remain noncommittal and make clear that they do not represent a particular bias, or endorse a particular doctrine.

A great deal of the necessary information might be elicited through detailed questionnaires, but this cannot take the place of field work by personnel with a background in automation engineering.

INDEX

217